Meteorology: An Introduction to the Wonders of the Weather

Robert G. Fovell, Ph.D.

THE GREAT COURSES®

PUBLISHED BY:

THE GREAT COURSES
Corporate Headquarters
4840 Westfields Boulevard, Suite 500
Chantilly, Virginia 20151-2299
Phone: 1-800-832-2412
Fax: 703-378-3819
www.thegreatcourses.com

Robert G. Fovell, Ph.D.

Professor of Atmospheric and Oceanic Sciences
University of California, Los Angeles

Professor Robert G. Fovell is Professor of Atmospheric and Oceanic Sciences at the University of California, Los Angeles, where he also serves as cofounder and cochair of the Interdepartmental Program in Mathematics/Atmospheric and Oceanic Sciences. He received his Ph.D. in Atmospheric Sciences from the University of Illinois at Urbana Champaign.

Among his many duties at UCLA, Professor Fovell serves as the chair of the Faculty Executive Committee of the College of Letters and Science and as faculty undergraduate advisor for Atmospheric and Oceanic Sciences. He is also affiliated with UCLA's Institute of the Environment and the Joint Institute for Regional Earth System Science and Engineering. Professor Fovell teaches courses in atmospheric dynamics and thermodynamics, numerical weather prediction, weather forecasting, and cloud dynamics, among other topics. In 2005, he was awarded a UCLA Distinguished Teaching Award (the Harvey L. Eby Award for the Art of Teaching).

Professor Fovell has published extensively, particularly on the subjects of squall lines and storm dynamics, and has served as an associate editor of the *Monthly Weather Review*. He has also appeared as a commentator for programs on the National Geographic Channel and the Discovery Channel. ∎

Table of Contents

Table of Contents

Table of Contents

Meteorology:
An Introduction to the Wonders of the Weather

Scope:

This course answers a number of questions that you may have wondered about since childhood: How high is the sky? Why can't we see at night? How do soda straws work? What causes the seasons? And most important: If you open the emergency exit door of an airplane in mid-flight, will you and everything else on the plane immediately fly out the opening?

The course begins with a theme that, at first glance, seems ridiculous: Nature abhors extremes. We can point to numerous extremes in nature, especially when it comes to the weather: rainfall of 450 inches a year in 1 location in India, typhoons with 250-mph winds, temperatures exceeding 130°F in Death Valley and dropping to −80°F in the Alaskan interior. As we'll learn, though, these extremes represent nature's intolerance of imbalance and her efforts to rectify it.

Lecture 1 introduces our theme and sketches out our approach to understanding the weather, while Lecture 2 builds a foundation for that understanding with the important concepts of temperature, pressure, and density. In Lectures 3 and 4, we look at the atmosphere, the ozone layer, and the greenhouse effect. In Lectures 5 and 6, we explore how heat moves around and see how the Santa Ana winds develop. Beginning with Lecture 7 and continuing into Lecture 8, we turn to the topic of atmospheric moisture and find out how air is brought to saturation. In Lectures 9 and 10, we introduce the air parcel as a useful concept for talking about clouds and learn how thunderstorms form and why they don't form as often as they could. Lectures 11 and 12 are devoted to 4 principal forces that determine when, where, and how quickly the winds blow.

In Lecture 13, we look at the 1-cell model and the 3-cell model of global atmospheric circulation. In Lecture 14, we see fronts in action and learn about the life cycle of extratropical cyclones that develop along them, while Lecture 15 shows us what's happening higher in the atmosphere that also affects these cyclones. Lecture 16 uses many of the concepts discussed to this point in the course to further explore vertical and horizontal wind shear, and Lecture 17 covers the influence of mountains on the atmosphere. With Lectures 18 and 19, we learn about radar and follow images of squall lines, thunderstorms, and tornadoes. Lecture 20 discusses the influence of the ocean on weather and climate and outlines the development and effects of El Niño. We continue with "wild weather" in Lectures 21 and 22, which explore tropical cyclones and lightning. Finally, in Lectures 23 and 24, we close the course with a look at forecasting and modeling and answer the important question about opening the airplane exit door in mid-flight. ■

Nature Abhors Extremes

Lecture 1

Nature abhors extremes. This is my motto, the lens through which I view the physical world around us. I would like you to consider this statement, but don't accept it uncritically. After all, it seems like a ridiculous statement.

Our theme for this course is that nature abhors extremes. At first glance, this statement seems ridiculous. Nature is replete with extremes, especially extremes of weather. As we'll see throughout the course, however, extremes occur as nature attempts to correct an imbalance or release stress. In this lecture, we'll touch on a few of the concepts we'll examine in greater detail throughout the course and look at what's been called the "perfect storm" to see the relationship between low pressure and wind speed and illustrate what happens along a front.

Consider the Earth/atmosphere/ocean system. The radiation from the Sun warms the ground, and the atmosphere is heated from below, which results in an imbalance: cold air, warm ground. Stress builds as nature tries to distribute the heat, resulting in a storm. Throughout this course, we look at examples that help us understand specific concepts. A can of electronic duster, for example, introduces us to heat conductivity, the ozone hole, greenhouse gases, heat transfer, adiabatic expansion cooling, diabatic processes, phase changes, latent heat, and other concepts.

As we'll see throughout the course, however, extremes occur as nature attempts to correct an imbalance or release stress.

Now, let's talk about water vapor and shear, 2 important ingredients in the storm recipe. Shear is wind change over a distance—wind speed, wind direction, or both. We're talking here about horizontal wind, which can have shear in both the vertical and the horizontal direction. An infrared satellite image shows horizontal wind shear as a series of hooks that grow in a chain. This is an example of a shear instability. Such instability creates spin. Let's now consider vertical wind shear. If you spill a heavy fluid on your kitchen table, it spreads, owing to its own weight, and the leading edge of the fluid is clearly defined. By spilling the liquid, you've made a front, which is a place where fluids of different density meet. In the example with cold and warm air, we see that the more dense cold air burrows beneath the less dense warm air, creating vertical shear and, in turn, spin.

Many of you may know what has been called the "perfect storm" from the movie and book of the same name. This storm caused hundreds of millions of dollars of damage from Florida to Maine in 1991. Tracking this storm at various times on a topographic map, we note that the sustained winds increase as the central pressure drops, but this relationship is not always perfect. Pressure is important, but pressure gradients (or differences) largely determine wind speed.

The perfect storm was a direct ancestor of another hurricane named Grace. Notice that the air flow around Grace is counterclockwise. The forces involved here are pressure gradient force, which drives the wind; Coriolis force; and the centripetal force. They combine to produce counterclockwise motion around cyclones (pressure lows), parallel to isobars (lines of equal sea-level pressure). The front we see is a meeting place between cold and warm air. As the storm develops, the cold polar air pushes southward, creating a cold front. To the east, warm air is gaining the upper hand, creating a warm front. Along the front, the spin is increasing, and spin creates low pressure. Further into the storm, the cold front and Grace are on a collision course. Meanwhile, a new cyclone has appeared between the cold and the warm fronts. This is the perfect storm.

Thirty hours later, Hurricane Grace is a memory, and the perfect storm is evolving a more complicated structure. Jumping ahead again, the perfect storm is sitting over the Gulf Stream, soaking up moisture and energy. It is now a tropical cyclone, a hurricane just like Grace. As for the front, new cyclones will form along it in other places at other times. This is a cycle that will never end.

Our course will consist of an inquisitive approach to the weather. We'll ask and answer many questions, such as the following: How do the winds blow? Why do they blow the way they do? How are storms formed? Why do storms exist? Our goal throughout the course will be to enhance our appreciation for nature by increasing our understanding of its design. ■

Questions to Consider

1. Would the spray can employed in this lecture have gotten cold upon release of its contents if it contained only compressed air?

2. Keeping my motto "Nature abhors extremes" in mind, identify non-meteorological situations of stress or imbalance that could provoke dramatic and perhaps deadly consequences as they strive to regain some kind of balance or equilibrium.

Temperature, Pressure, and Density
Lecture 2

In this lecture, we'll consider 3 important concepts: temperature, pressure, and density. We'll see what temperature really measures, why pressure decreases with height, and why density is often the overlooked crucial factor. We'll also see how they're interrelated with the simple, powerful ideal gas law. Finally, we'll consider the implications of nature's desire to move mass from higher to lower pressure and look at the important concept of hydrostatic balance.

Let's begin with temperature. Temperature is the microscopic kinetic energy of atoms and molecules, which vibrate and translate even in solids, so long as the temperature is above absolute zero. At absolute zero (-273°C, -459°F, and 0°Kelvin), all microscopic motion ceases. Pressure is the force per unit area. To create pressure, we apply force. In the atmosphere, force is largely gravity due to the weight of air. Sea level pressure is 15 pounds per square inch, or 30 inches of mercury, or 1000 millibars.

To a large degree, pressure represents the weight of down-lying air; therefore, pressure decreases with height. As we ascend in the atmosphere, more of the mass of the atmosphere is below us and less is above, so the pressure pushing down on us decreases. Because we know that pressure is proportional to mass, this means that half the mass of the atmosphere is between 1000 and 500 millibars, and 80% of the mass is between 1000 and 200 millibars.

Density is mass divided by volume, usually measured as kilograms per cubic meter. For gases like air, temperature, pressure, and density are related through the ideal gas law: $p = \rho rt$. Here, p is pressure, measured in pascals; ρ is density; t is temperature in the Kelvin scale; and r is a proportionality constant. The ideal gas law implies that temperature, pressure, and density are not independent; changing one changes one or both of the others. If we hold density constant, increasing temperature causes pressure to rise. If we hold pressure fixed, as temperature rises, density decreases. This means that at the same pressure, warm air is less dense than cold air. This is crucial because fluids with different densities resist mixing. In the atmosphere, fronts represent the meeting places between air masses that have different densities. They push against each other, in part, because they resist mixing.

What is the pressure measure known as the inch of mercury? The inventor of the barometer was Evangelista Torricelli in the 1600s, but you make a barometer of sorts every time you drink water through a straw. If you want to drink out of a straw from a glass of water, you have to create a vacuum. Once the vacuum is created, the atmosphere does the job of pushing water up into the straw from below. The difference between the top and the base of the fluid column indicates how much force is pressing down on the outside of the straw. Force per unit area is pressure. At standard sea level pressure of 1000 millibars, the atmosphere can support a water column 33 feet high. But rather than use a water column, Torricelli employed mercury for his barometer. Sea level pressure can support a mercury column 30 inches high, hence the unit of pressure.

Nature seeks to move mass from high to low pressure. This means nature wants the water to rise in the straw, but it doesn't. Why not?

Note that pressure differences can exist in all directions, as you can see in the familiar phenomenon of trapping fluid inside a straw with your finger. Nature seeks to move mass from high to low pressure. This means nature wants the water to rise in the straw, but it doesn't. Why not? The missing piece is that water itself has weight, and this weight is pushing downward, due to gravity. Here's another key concept: If a fluid is not accelerating, then the forces must be balanced. The primary balance here is the pressure difference acting upward and the gravity force pulling down. This is a stalemate we call "hydrostatic balance." The straw is sealed, and we have hydrostatic balance, 2 powerful opposing forces, but no net motion.

When you remove your finger, the forces come into balance, and the water flows out. ■

Suggested Reading

Turner, *Scientific Instruments 1500–1900.*

Questions to Consider

1. We have described pressure as largely being the weight of the overlying air. Actually, anything above us should increase the downward force. But, if that's true, why aren't we discomfited, or even crushed, when a large, very heavy airplane flies overhead? Hint: It has nothing to do with lift.

2. On very hot days, jumbo jets are not permitted to take off or land at some airports, owing to insufficiently long runways. Why?

Atmosphere—Composition and Origin
Lecture 3

In this lecture, we'll see that the variation of temperature with height is complex. We'll learn what air is made of, now and in the distant past as well, and we'll be introduced to the greenhouse effect and its major players.

Think about these questions as we go through the lecture: Is it always true that warm air rises and cold air sinks? Could something that makes up only 4 out of every 10,000 molecules in air really make a difference? What good is the ozone layer, and how did a chemical used in common spray cans damage it?

The atmosphere has 4 layers, distinguished by how temperature varies with height. The lowest layer is called the troposphere; this is our weather sphere. It extends from sea level up to about 7.5 miles. Surface pressure is 1000 millibars, and the pressure at the top of the troposphere (the tropopause) is about 200 millibars. Notice that temperature decreases very quickly with height—from 60°F at the bottom to −80°F at the top.

The next layer is the stratosphere. This is a layer of great stability that impedes vertical motion. The stratopause is about 30 miles above sea level, with pressure of about 1 millibar. In this layer, temperature increases with height instead of decreasing. Next is the mesosphere. Here, temperature resumes its decrease with height. The mesopause is 55 miles above sea level, and the pressure there is 0.01 millibars. Finally, the thermosphere extends from 55 miles up to where the atmosphere just fades away. Temperatures there can be thousands of degrees, yet the thermosphere is also a cold place. There's virtually no mass in the thermosphere, but it's a deep layer.

We can divide air into 2 categories, dry air and water vapor. Dry air is largely fixed in quantity and well mixed through the atmosphere. Water vapor, in contrast, is extremely variable—in horizontal space, in vertical depth, and in time.

Dry air is 78% nitrogen in the form N_2, 21% oxygen in the form O_2, and 1% argon. Other minor constituents of the dry atmospheric mass include carbon dioxide, CO_2. Carbon dioxide represents 0.0387% of the dry atmospheric mass, but it has an outsized importance as a greenhouse gas and plays a major role in regulating the temperature of the Earth's surface. Another

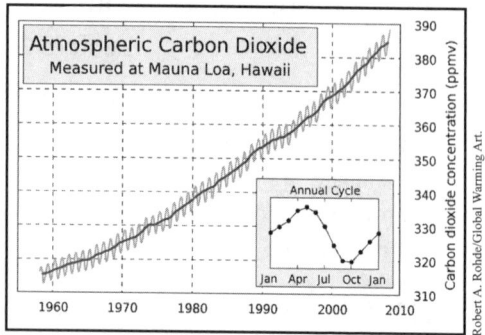

The Keeling curve plots atmospheric CO_2 concentration against time.

minor constituent in the dry atmospheric mass is methane, CH_4, which is about 2 parts per million. Methane is roughly 25 times more potent per unit weight than carbon dioxide as a greenhouse gas and is also increasing over time. Other minor constituents include nitrous oxide, N_2O, and ozone, O_3. The majority of ozone is in the stratosphere, where local concentrations are 250 times larger than they are in the atmosphere as a whole.

Dry air is largely fixed in quantity and well mixed through the atmosphere. Water vapor, in contrast, is extremely variable, in horizontal space, in vertical depth, and in time.

Let's look at the natural stratospheric ozone cycle. The act of absorbing ultraviolet radiation causes an oxygen molecule to split into its individual atoms, which will quickly find a nearby O_2 molecule to form O_3. Next, ozone absorbs ultraviolet radiation, which splits it apart. In this process, ozone is both created and destroyed, but there's no net loss.

The ozone hole is an area of depleted stratospheric ozone residing over the South Pole. Excessive ozone hole expansion is caused mainly by chlorofluorocarbons, or CFCs. CFCs play a dual role as greenhouse molecules and destroyers of stratospheric ozone. Because CFCs are chemically inert, they have very long lifetimes, which allows them to spread globally and loft far upward, reaching the stratosphere. Ultraviolet radiation from the Sun can break CFC molecules apart, liberating the chlorine atoms. Satellite images show considerable inter-annual variability in the ozone hole, but the trend toward larger and deeper ozone holes is clear.

Let's turn to water vapor. Water vapor represents 0% to 4% of the total atmospheric mass but is extremely variable in space and time. Water vapor is concentrated near the Earth's surface and the lower troposphere. The ability of air to hold water vapor is a strong function of temperature. Warm air can hold much more water vapor than cold air. As we have seen, temperature decreases rapidly with height in the lower atmosphere. This is one reason why most of the water vapor is located near the ground.

Earth didn't always have the atmosphere we have today. The early Earth probably had an atmosphere of hydrogen and helium, but Earth's gravity is not strong enough to retain those elements. Later, Earth developed an atmosphere that had significantly more CO_2 than our present atmosphere and virtually no oxygen. In our atmosphere, the first free oxygen probably resulted from photodissociation of water vapor by intense solar radiation. Significant oxygen concentrations had to await the evolution of photosynthesis. ∎

Questions to Consider

1. Why does the ozone hole disappear in summertime?

2. The ionosphere is not an atmospheric layer, but rather a region that extends from the upper mesosphere up to 400 kilometers or so. The structure of this region varies dramatically from day to night. Strong solar radiation ionizes atoms, creating layers that absorb AM radio signals but disappear at night. At what time of day do you expect to be most successful at receiving a distant AM station on your radio?

Radiation and the Greenhouse Effect
Lecture 4

In this particular lecture, we'll see that all objects emit radiation, but the amount and type of radiation depends very strongly on temperature. We'll see what solar radiation is made of, and why the radiation produced by the Earth is so very different. We'll discuss absorption and see that some objects are indiscriminate absorbers, while others are very selective.

L et's begin with the electromagnetic spectrum. The electromagnetic spectrum consists of radiation we can see (visible light), radiation we can feel (infrared), radiation we can exploit (microwaves for cooking and communication), and radiation we can largely do without (X-rays, gamma rays, and much of the ultraviolet). The electromagnetic spectrum spans an enormous range of wavelengths. For this course, our focus is on the ultraviolet, the visible, and the near and far infrared.

We can identify 4 fundamental facts concerning radiation: (1) All objects emit radiation. (2) The total amount of radiative energy emitted is a very strong function of temperature. (3) All objects radiate energy at all wavelengths of the electromagnetic spectrum. (4) Objects radiate more energy at some wavelengths than others.

Knowing that both the amount and kind of radiation produced depend on temperature leads us to 2 more laws. Planck's law tells us how much of each kind of radiation an object produces. Wien's law shows us which radiation wavelength is produced the most. For an object with about the same temperature as the Sun's outer surface, the Planck curve looks like a bell curve; the total radiative energy is the area beneath the curve, with the peak in the visible portion of the spectrum. For a cooler object, the area beneath the curve is smaller, and the peak is shifted to the right, to longer wavelengths of visible light. According to Wien's law, the wavelength of maximum emission is inversely proportional to temperature. The Earth's surface typically produces negligible amounts of radiation at visible and ultraviolet wavelengths, which is why we can't see at night.

Let's now turn to emission and absorption. We see the Planck curves for the Sun and the Earth plotted on the same scale. Even though the Sun is much hotter, the curves have equal height. The explanation for this is twofold. First, solar radiation is spread throughout space. Second, our "radiation budget" is balanced. The energy we receive from the Sun and the energy we lose to the cold of space are equal. This is important for thermal equilibrium. Note that there is virtually no overlap between these 2 curves, a fact which leads to the greenhouse effect.

Radiation can be reflected back to its origin, it can be scattered in all directions, or it can be absorbed. The only way radiation can change the temperature of an object is through absorption.

What is the fate of radiation, whether it's shortwave from the Sun or longwave from the Earth? Radiation can be reflected back to its origin, it can be scattered in all directions, or it can be absorbed. The only way radiation can change the temperature of an object is through absorption. Atoms and molecules absorb wavelengths for which they have a particular affinity. Objects that absorb everything are called blackbodies. The Earth's surface is very nearly a blackbody, while atmospheric gases tend to be very selective absorbers.

A diagram of atmospheric absorption introduces us to the greenhouse effect. Absorption of incoming solar radiation is limited but important. Much of that radiation survives to be absorbed by the ground. That radiation is then reradiated upward at longer wavelengths. Much of that radiation, though, is absorbed by water vapor and carbon dioxide on the way out. Our primary greenhouse gases are very selective absorbers, and this differential absorption represents the greenhouse effect. If we were to remove these gases from our atmosphere, the Earth would be a much colder place.

Let's look at the atmosphere's greenhouse effect in a different way. Picture sunlight streaming through the atmosphere. Visible, ultraviolet, and near infrared are largely ignored by the finicky atmosphere but absorbed by the ground, warming the Earth. The Earth radiates longer wavelengths. Some of the outgoing radiation escapes to space, but some is absorbed by the greenhouse gases.

The greenhouse gases themselves radiate in all directions, including downward. The ground absorbs that radiation and, in turn, must emit some. Some of that radiation escapes into space, and some is absorbed by the greenhouse gases. Each step in the process actually involves less energy. We're moving toward equilibrium, but the temperature of that equilibrium is much higher than if none of the extra greenhouse action had taken place. The presence of greenhouse gases has made the Earth much warmer than it otherwise would have been. They serve as our thermostat; hence our concern about their quantities. ■

Questions to Consider

1. The Sun, as seen from space, is a yellow-white star. Of course, the Sun generates all colors of light, but yellow predominates. As the Sun ages and cools, will its light become more reddish or more bluish? Why?

2. Consider a conventional incandescent light bulb with clear glass that is connected to a source of electricity controlled via a dimmer switch. Turn on the light and slowly rotate the switch, allowing more current to pass through the circuit. At first, the bulb's filament glows a deep red, then a bright orange, then an even brighter yellow before glowing very bright white. Explain this color-shifting phenomenon.

3. Compared to Mercury, Venus is located almost twice as far from the Sun and receives only a fraction of the solar radiation. Yet its surface temperatures are hotter than Mercury's. Why?

Sphericity, Conduction, and Convection
Lecture 5

Before we review, I have a few questions for you. What causes the seasons? (Here's a hint: Most Harvard graduates get this one wrong.) Why does a metal spoon feel cooler than a drinking glass, when both have the same temperature? When we touch it with our hand, why do we tend to dramatically underestimate the temperature of the sea?

et's review what we've learned so far. Temperature differences make pressure differences. Pressure differences drive winds. The intent of winds is to reduce the temperature differences that gave rise to the pressure differences. Two major sources of temperature difference are unequal heating of the Earth's surface and seasonal variation. The temperature difference is relatively smaller in the summer than the winter, owing to obliquity (the tilt of the Earth's axis), but at no time is the pole warmer than the equator. The average equator-to-pole temperature difference during wintertime is almost 100°F. It seems, then, that nature isn't very efficient in reducing temperature differences through winds.

Let's consider 2 other mechanisms of heat transfer: conduction and convection, both of which require a medium. Heat is a flow of energy between objects. Conduction is heat transfer by direct atomic contact. It operates in one direction, from warm to cold. Conduction involves transferring microscopic kinetic energy, as measured by temperature, from an object with more to an object with less. Objects differ in their ability to conduct heat. A metal spoon, for example, feels cooler than a drinking glass, even if they're both at room temperature, because metal is a good conductor of heat.

You're perfectly comfortable in 70°F air, but if you were immersed in water at that same temperature, you would feel very cold. Why? Water at that temperature is 26 times better at conducting heat than air is, and since the temperature of the water is lower than your body temperature, you're losing heat to the surroundings. Air is a terrible conductor of heat but a good insulator. This is why beach sand can get very hot on a sunny afternoon, while the air a few millimeters above it is much cooler.

In thinking about heat transfer, we also need to look at the concept of thermal inertia, that is, resistance to temperature change. Objects with high thermal inertia can absorb a lot of energy without their temperatures rising very much. Note that heat conductivity and thermal inertia are not the same thing. The afternoon sand on the beach feels hot because it is a good conductor, and it gives you its heat very quickly. The sand is hot because its thermal inertia is low. In contrast to the temperature of sand, which has a wide-ranging diurnal cycle, the temperature of the sea surface doesn't change much during the day. Part of the reason for this is that the sunlight warms up the surface of the water, but then that water is circulated internally. If air were a better conductor of heat, the sand on the beach would not get as hot as it does because the air would take heat away from the sand more quickly.

If air were a better conductor of heat, the sand on the beach would not get as hot as it does because the air would take heat away from the sand more quickly.

Given that air is not a good conductor, heat transfer in any direction needs some help. That help comes from convection: heat transport by mass fluid motion. In this course, heat transport basically means wind. One way that the wind can cause vertical mixing and vertical heat transport occurs as it courses over irregular surfaces. This creates eddies that transport hot air up from the ground and cooler air down to the surface. The same thing can occur as air passes over land that has been irregularly heated. Looking at a temperature profile with height for a windy day, we see that the temperature near the ground is lower than it would be if the air were calm.

On the beach, sand's low thermal inertia permits the sand to get cold at night, chilling the air near the ground, and the warmth from above is not conducted downward very quickly. This results in a temperature inversion, or a radiation inversion, when temperature increases with height. Under what conditions are we most likely to get really cold temperatures at the ground? There are 4: low humidity, a clear rather than cloudy sky, low thermal inertia of the surface, and calm winds.

Temperature differences play a critical role in meteorology. One way to create temperature differences is to provide surfaces that differ in some critical aspect. Suppose they receive more or less solar radiation, owing to Earth's curvature and tilt. They might also differ in how they absorb solar radiation due to differences in reflectants. One way to mitigate temperature differences created by differences in latitude, season, or surface characteristics is to transport heat by mass fluid motion—by convection. ■

Questions to Consider

1. Seasons are caused by the fact that the Earth's axis is tilted. Presently, that tilt is 23.5 degrees, but this value varies over a long period of time. When would you expect an ice age to be most likely, when the tilt is greater than the present value or smaller? Why?

2. Consider a blanket of snow on the ground. It is often noticed that snow melts faster from below than above, resulting in air pockets beneath the crust that cause the snow to crunch when you walk on it. Why?

Sea Breezes and Santa Anas
Lecture 6

Temperature differences make pressure differences, and pressure differences drive winds. In this lecture, we will see how local temperature differences, such as between land and sea, can create a local circulation, the sea breeze.

The purpose of these winds is to reduce the temperature differences that gave rise to them. As always, here are a couple of questions to think about during the lecture: We've heard that heat flows from warm to cold; how is it, then, that we experience cold winds? Which would be better in eliminating temperature differences, blowing warm air to a cold place or blowing cold air to a warm place?

Let's begin by revisiting pressure. Pressure largely reflects the weight of overlying air, owing to gravity, and is proportional to mass. Therefore, pressure decreases with height. Surface pressure is approximately 1000 millibars, and 50% of the atmospheric mass resides between the levels of 1000 and 500 millibars. We know that pressure decreases with height; note, too, that pressure decreases with height faster in colder air.

Let's see how temperature differences make pressure differences. If we increase the temperature on one side of the space between the 2 isobars, the 500-millibar isobar rises higher above the ground. The layer of air between the 2 isobars is thicker because the temperature is warmer. Let's pick a point and draw a line along the 500-millibar level, then look toward the colder air. Both isobars are beneath the line, so the pressure at this point is lower than 500 millibars. Looking toward the warmer air, the 500-millibar level is above our line; the pressure is higher than 500 millibars there.

We have relatively higher pressure at the same level in the warmer region; we have relatively lower pressure at the same level in the colder region. Pressure differences like this create winds. Here, the air within the warm region rises up and diverges out of that region. Mass is leaving this relatively warmer region. And since there's less mass in that region, the surface pressure is dropping. The warmer air is moving toward the colder region, adding mass to that region and causing the surface pressure there to rise. This tilts the 1000-millibar isobar, leaving us with relatively higher pressure where it's colder near the surface and relatively lower pressure where it's warmer near the surface. We've created a circulation.

Let's apply this model to the sea breeze. The ocean absorbs more solar radiation during the day than the sand does because it's darker. But the ocean isn't hotter than the sand, because it has an internal circulation and because liquid water has significant thermal inertia. Looking at the sea breeze circulation, we see warm air rising over the heated land and cool air sinking over the cooler ocean. The surface sea breeze is blowing inland from the cooler sea to the warmer land. A topographic map of the city of Los Angeles shows the increase in the wind from sea to land over the course of a day. If the land surface becomes colder at night, the circulation will reverse, and a land breeze will develop.

How do these breezes work to decrease temperature differences? To answer this question, think of eating hot soup in a cold room. The soup loses heat energy to the room air via conduction, but the air doesn't carry the heat away very efficiently. As a result, the temperature difference between the soup and the air decreases as a function of time. This, in turn, decreases the heat loss because heat loss is proportional to temperature difference. There are at least 2 other mechanisms for helping to reduce the land/sea temperature difference operating in this case: (1) Mixing land and sea air moderates the temperatures of both,

The ocean absorbs more solar radiation during the day than the sand does because it's darker. But the ocean isn't hotter than the sand, because it has an internal circulation and because liquid water has significant thermal inertia.

reducing the temperature difference from land to sea, and (2) changing the elevation of air changes its temperature. Specifically, air warms in descent. The temperature change is due to volume change alone, without the addition or removal of heat. This is called the dry adiabatic process. In general, rising air cools, and sinking air warms up. Thus, the vertical motions in the sea breeze work to decrease the temperature difference that drove the circulation to begin with.

The Santa Ana winds of southern California blow dry, hot, and fast. Most Santa Ana events start with cold, dense air spilling down across the Great Basin of Nevada and Utah. The southward progress toward

Image courtesy of Dr. Robert Fovell.

The Santa Ana winds fan regional wildfires in southern California.

Los Angeles is partially stopped by a ring of mountains surrounding the Los Angeles basin. When the cold air reaches the mountains, the flow is restricted, but the wind that escapes is blowing at a higher velocity. As it descends into the basin, the air experiences compression and is warmed at a rate of 30°F per mile, or 10°C per kilometer.

Ascending air cools at the same rate, 10°C per kilometer, which is a ratio of 2 numbers: g, the acceleration of gravity, and cp, a measure of thermal inertia. The value g tells us how quickly an object in freefall gains velocity on descent: 32 feet (or 10 meters) per second squared. The value cp is the specific heat of the air at constant pressure. In the metric system, cp is 1004 joules per kilogram. The rate of 10°C per kilometer thus reflects the Earth's mass and composition. ■

Questions to Consider

1. Is the dry adiabatic lapse rate also 10°C per kilometer (30°F per mile) on Venus, Mars, or Jupiter? Why or why not?

2. How would the Santa Ana winds be different if you flattened the topography of the western United States?

An Introduction to Atmospheric Moisture
Lecture 7

Some questions to think about during this lecture: When are we susceptible to getting static electric shocks when we shuffle around in stocking feet, and why? Why can ice appear on airplane wings? Shouldn't ice just bounce off? Why are clouds the likely result of forcing air to ascend?

In the last lecture, we examined sea breeze and land breeze circulations. We also learned that the Santa Anas are hot because of downslope motion and fast because they're channeled through the mountains. In this lecture, we'll look at atmospheric moisture to find out why the Santa Ana winds are dry.

Water vapor is a great place to start our exploration of humidity. The ability of air to hold water vapor is a strong function of temperature. Warm air can hold more water vapor than cold air, which explains why most vapor is located close to the ground. A sample of air has 2 moisture properties—vapor capacity (VC), which tells us how much water vapor air can hold at a maximum, and vapor supply (VS), which tells us how much water vapor exists in the sample. A sample of air with 10 grams of water vapor per kilogram of dry air would have a vapor supply of 10 grams per kilogram (10 g/kg). Relative humidity, or RH, is the ratio of vapor supply and capacity expressed as a percentage.

Vapor supply is a measure of absolute humidity, which is primarily a function of temperature. For each increase of 10°C, vapor capacity approximately doubles. It doesn't take much water vapor to saturate cold air, and if extra water vapor is present, it forms liquid or ice.

The Santa Ana winds become hot due to the dry adiabatic process, which involves temperature change from volume contraction rather than heat exchange. A sample of descending dry air will heat at a rate of 10°C per kilometer. Moist air—that is, air with some vapor supply—also compresses dry adiabatically, as long as the air is cloud-free. As the moist air moves downslope, its vapor capacity increases dramatically, due to compression warming and the exponential relationship between vapor capacity and temperature. As a Santa Ana wind moves downslope, both its temperature and its vapor capacity increase, but the vapor supply remains the same; thus, the relative humidity drops.

Indoor relative humidity can become uncomfortably low in the winter, resulting in static electric shocks. Under higher humidity conditions, electric charge can't build up because objects are coated with a very thin layer of surface water. Even if the water content of air doesn't change, relative humidity will change with temperature: Relative humidity will be highest when the temperature is lowest.

Water molecules are always in collision. The lower the temperature, the less likely it is that 2 vapor molecules can avoid bonding when they collide, so the drops they form are more likely to be long-lived.

Let's make a cloud by doing our Santa Ana example in reverse. Suppose air starts at the foot of a 2-mile mountain under these conditions: temperature, 110°F; vapor capacity, more than 50 g/kg; and vapor supply, 8 g/kg (relative humidity under 16%). Forcing that air to ascend the mountain decreases the temperature and the vapor capacity. With just a 2-mile lift, we can bring the air to saturation through expansion cooling.

Why does vapor capacity increase with temperature? The answer involves the temperature of water molecules and the pressure they exert. The 3 phases of any substance are vapor, solid, and liquid. We'll consider vapor and liquid at temperatures above freezing. Water molecules are always in collision. The lower the temperature, the less likely it is that 2 vapor molecules can avoid bonding when they collide, so the drops they form are more likely to be long-lived.

The higher the temperature, the more likely it is that a water molecule can escape from its liquid prison and become vapor. Water vapor molecules in the vicinity of a plain surface of liquid water, such as a lake or a pond, exert a pressure on the liquid water surface, known as vapor pressure. Vapor molecules in motion may become incorporated into the liquid water surface (condensing), while water molecules in the surface seek to return to the atmosphere as vapor (evaporating). When the rates of condensation and evaporation are the same, the vapor liquid system is in equilibrium, also called saturation. To reiterate, actual vapor pressure is measured by the vapor supply; saturation vapor pressure is measured by the vapor capacity. These concepts are expressed as mass or quantity, rather than pressure.

As the temperature gets higher, more vapor molecules are needed to balance the escapees. That balance is saturation, and the saturation vapor pressure and vapor capacity increase quickly with temperature. In a nutshell, the ability of air to hold water vapor is really the ability of vapor to avoid condensing and succeed in evaporating.

How does the condensation process start? Vapor molecules require a surface to condense on, such as grit suspended in midair. Such surfaces are called condensation nuclei. Condensation particles start off as small cloud droplets that fall very slowly relative to still air. But collisions among these droplets can result in larger, faster-falling drops, which may grow by accreting the smaller particles.

To become ice, liquid water needs an ice nucleus, but ice nuclei are not as common as we might expect. Liquid water drops, called supercool liquid, can persist in subfreezing temperatures. The Bergeron, or ice crystal, process for precipitation production is based on the fact that ice crystals will grow rapidly at the expense of supercool drops once they manage to form. The saturation vapor pressure over ice is smaller than that over water, allowing ice to survive in conditions that would cause liquid water to disappear. In a nutshell, ice outcompetes liquid in subfreezing temperatures, but it starts with a disadvantage—a lack of ice nuclei to kickstart the process. Cloud seeding represents an attempt to supply the missing ice nuclei. ∎

Vonnegut, *Cat's Cradle*.

Questions to Consider

1. True or false: Water vapor can condense to liquid in sub-saturated air. Why?

2. In the premier episode of the TV series *Star Trek: Voyager*, a powerful entity said he performed an experiment on a populated planet that inadvertently rendered it a desert. His experiment removed all particles from the planet's atmosphere that permitted water vapor to condense upon them, permanently ending the possibility of rainfall on the planet. Does this scenario make sense?

Bringing Air to Saturation
Lecture 8

Actually, our familiar temperature is also known as a "dry bulb temperature" because it's measured with a thermometer bulb that is not wet. We'll see what makes the wet bulb wet pretty soon, but first, I want to talk about the dew point temperature, and I'd like to do that via a story.

In the last lecture, we introduced the central issue of atmospheric moisture, and we saw how to saturate air through expansion cooling. In this lecture, we will see 2 more ways of bringing air to saturation, and we'll encounter 2 new kinds of temperature. Along the way, we'll consider a few questions: What is black ice, and when and where does it form? Why are ice cubes you make in your freezer so often cloudy in the center? And why does it take food longer to cook at higher elevations?

Let's review vapor supply and vapor capacity. Vapor supply (VS) is the amount of water vapor in air, expressed as grams of water vapor per kilogram of dry air. Vapor capacity (VC) represents the amount of water vapor air can hold at a maximum. The ability of air to hold water vapor is a strong function of temperature.

In addition to the dry adiabatic process, there are 2 other ways to saturate air, which introduces us to the dew point temperature and the wet bulb temperature. We can understand the dew point if we think about a cold can of soda "sweating" on a hot day. As we have seen, the regular, or dry bulb, temperature tells us the vapor capacity of air. The dew point temperature tells us the air's vapor supply. At saturation, vapor supply and capacity are the same, so the temperature and the dew point are also the same.

We can bring air to saturation without changing its vapor content or pressure by extracting heat. This is a diabatic process. When the temperature of air is decreased to its dew point, saturation is reached. Suppose we have a subsaturated sample of air. If the temperature is higher than the dew point, the vapor supply is less than the vapor capacity. If we decrease the temperature of the air, the vapor capacity decreases and the relative humidity increases. When the relative humidity reaches 100%, any further cooling will make the air supersaturated, and condensation will appear. The dew point approach to saturation—isobaric cooling—does not change the vapor supply.

On most nights after sundown, the temperature of air near the ground cools, decreasing the vapor capacity. If the air cools to its dew point, condensation will form, using the ground surface as condensation nuclei. Dew or frost typically forms around sunrise and on objects with low thermal inertia, such as car windows and concrete bridges. Black ice is a particularly dangerous kind of ice that forms on roadways when subfreezing air is chilled to the dew or frost point. Here's a forecasting rule: If the air mass at your location is not expected to change overnight, the minimum temperature will probably be no lower than the afternoon dew point. If the air is cooled overnight to the dew point, further cooling will be more difficult because there is resistance to cooling in the form of condensation warming.

Evaporation is a cooling process. When you climb out of a swimming pool, you feel cold because the liquid water on your skin is evaporating into subsaturated air. It takes energy—heat coming from you—to break the bonds that hold water molecules together into liquid water drops. The water evaporates because the air is subsaturated and the vapor supply is less than the vapor capacity. As evaporation proceeds, the number of vapor molecules around your skin increases, and the vapor supply and pressure both increase. As the difference between the vapor supply and the vapor capacity gets smaller, evaporation and the cooling it produces slow down.

On most nights after sundown, the temperature of air near the ground cools, decreasing the vapor capacity. If the air cools to its dew point, condensation will form, using the ground surface as condensation nuclei.

Saturation by evaporation cooling and the subsequent moistening is the wet bulb approach to saturation. We cannot bring a subsaturated sample of air to saturation through evaporation, because evaporating water takes energy from the air cooling it, and as the air cools, the vapor capacity decreases. As we evaporate water into the air sample, the water vapor content and the vapor supply increase, but the temperature and the vapor capacity decrease. At some point, the temperature and the dew point will meet at a new temperature, called the wet bulb.

We've looked at 3 temperatures: actual, dew point, and wet bulb. The actual temperature tells us vapor capacity. The dew point tells us vapor supply and shows how much we can cool the air without changing the vapor supply before saturation is reached. The wet bulb temperature tells us how much we can cool the air by evaporation. At saturation, all 3 temperatures are equal.

Boiling is actually rapid evaporation. A bubble that forms in a pot of boiling water is subject to pressure from both the atmosphere and the liquid water. The boiling point is the temperature at which saturation vapor pressure pushing out from the bubble matches the external pressure pushing back. The fact that pressure decreases with height explains why the boiling point decreases with elevation above sea level.

This illustrates an important point: Phase changes occur at constant temperature, as well as constant pressure. The phase transition between solid and liquid water also involves latent heating and cooling. This is called the latent heat of fusion or melting, depending on the direction of the process. One of the principal roles of clouds is to transport heat vertically, with latent heat release fueling potentially powerful updrafts. Whether clouds can accomplish this, however, depends on how stable the environment is. ∎

1. You are taking a shower with warm water, some of which is evaporating into the room air. You notice that before the room air becomes noticeably foggy, condensation has already begun forming on your bathroom mirror. Why?

2. Under what atmospheric and surface conditions are we likely to get frost on the ground?

Lecture 8: Bringing Air to Saturation

Clouds, Stability, and Buoyancy, Part 1
Lecture 9

In this lecture, we commence a detailed examination of clouds: how they come about; why are they thick or thin, long-lived or short. We'll introduce the very useful concept of the air parcel, a blob of air that we'll follow around and monitor its temperature and humidity.

During this lecture, think about why the bitterly cold air of the upper troposphere isn't exchanged with warm air at the ground. Clouds are dynamic and come in many shapes and sizes. Mounded clouds with substantial vertical development are called cumulus clouds. Lenticular (lens-shaped) clouds sometimes look like flying saucers and result from lifting moist air near mountains. Rotor clouds are the end result of violent downslope winds.

Clouds are classified with respect to the height of the cloud base—low, middle, or high. "Strato" is the first prefix used to indicate cloud base height. Stratus are low clouds, spread out and straight. "Alto" is the prefix used for middle-level clouds, and high clouds are cirrus, or "cirro." Two suffixes indicate the degree of vertical development. These prefixes and suffixes

Image courtesy of Dr. Robert Fovell.

Lenticular clouds can look like flying saucers and sometimes are mistaken for them.

can be combined to describe clouds: cirrostratus, altocumulus, and so on. The recipe for clouds has 2 ingredients: moisture and phase changes, and atmospheric stability and instability.

Let's consider a parcel of dry air. We assume that it has flexible sides, so the inside pressure adjusts as the outside pressure changes. We also assume that the parcel is closed and insulated; it experiences no mass or energy transfer with the environment. If a parcel is dry, closed, and insulated, there's no way to change its temperature except by changing the outside pressure.

Image courtesy of Dr. Robert Fovell.

Rotor clouds are the result of violent downslope winds.

A lapse rate quantifies how temperature changes with height. Our expectation is that temperature decreases with height, resulting in a positive lapse rate. If we lift a subsaturated air parcel, it cools at a rate of 10°C per kilometer solely due to expansion. This is the dry adiabatic lapse rate (DALR). We saw that temperature tends to decrease significantly with height in the troposphere. This environmental lapse rate (ELR) is, on average, 6.5°C per kilometer in the troposphere. ELR varies in both vertical and horizontal space and in time. Lapse rates will ultimately tell us if clouds are positively or negatively buoyant.

Let's return to our dry air parcel. How temperature varies inside the parcel depends on expansion cooling, the constant DALR. How temperature varies outside the parcel is governed by the variable ELR. Consider an air parcel that is 15°F warmer than the outside air. It's the same pressure as its surroundings but much less dense. It is positively buoyant and wants to rise. As it rises, it undergoes expansion cooling at the DALR, 30°F per mile. At 1 mile up, the parcel has cooled to 75°F in an environment of 70°F. By 2 miles up, the parcel is colder than its environment: inside temperature, 45°F; outside temperature, 50°F.

Up to this point, what's taking place is free convection (heat transport by fluid motion). Further ascent can only occur if the parcel is forced—forced convection. If the parcel were forced to rise much farther, it would become much colder and much denser than its surroundings. In reality, the parcel will likely remain in the environment where its inside and outside temperatures match.

How can nature share all the hot air near the surface with the bitterly cold tropopause, just a few miles above?

How can nature share all the hot air near the surface with the bitterly cold tropopause, just a few miles above? We've seen that we can't lift hot air very far; it doesn't stay hot. This illustrates an important concept called atmospheric stability—resistance to vertical displacement. If we loft a parcel of air, its density increases at the same pressure, and it becomes negatively buoyant. If we push the parcel down, its density decreases at the same pressure, and it becomes positively buoyant. This situation is called absolutely stable. The airplane example helps illustrate why the troposphere doesn't turn over. If we drag the tropopause air down to the surface, it gets much hotter, much less dense at the same pressure, than the air that's already there.

Nature's way of lofting surface air to the tropopause is thunderstorms. Rising air expands and cools because pressure decreases with height (dry adiabatic process). The relative humidity of rising moist air also increases. That's how we created a cloud from lifting, because vapor capacity decreases quickly as temperature goes up. Further lifting of saturated air means further expansion cooling, but now there's a vapor excess (supersaturation). Some of that excess vapor must condense, and condensation is a warming process. What receives the warming? The air in the supersaturated parcel.

The net result is that the cooling rate for the parcel on ascent is cut in half, to 5°C per kilometer. This is the moist adiabatic lapse rate (MALR). Unlike the DALR, the MALR is not a constant. Let's look at a saturated parcel of air. It starts at the same initial temperature as its environment, 30°C, and holds 28 g/kg of water vapor. If we push that parcel up 1 kilometer, it cools at only

5°C. The parcel is now 1°C warmer than its new environment and positively buoyant. At 2 kilometers, the saturated parcel is now 2°C warmer and rising faster.

The ELR, usually 6°C per kilometer, is actually larger than the MALR, 5°C per kilometer, so the rising saturated parcel can become warmer than its environment. And the farther it rises, the more its temperature increases in relation to its environment. The reason the atmosphere isn't always in a state of chaotic mixing is that we don't encounter saturated air near the surface very often. Air typically starts off subsaturated and cooling faster than the ELR before finally reaching saturation. ■

Questions to Consider

1. You are driving in your car, and suddenly your windows start fogging up from the inside. Is it better to turn on the defrost heater or the air conditioner? What does each device do to the car interior's air?

2. On very humid days, we often say the air "feels" heavy. Is moist air denser than dry air at the same temperature? Hint: Adding water vapor to the air increases the value of the "gas constant" r in the ideal gas law: $p = \rho r t$, where p = pressure, ρ = density, t = temperature, and r is the gas constant.

Clouds, Stability, and Buoyancy, Part 2
Lecture 10

In this lecture, we continue our discussion of clouds, stability, and buoyancy. We will discovery why it matters if condensed vapor remains in the parcel as cloud water or falls out as rain. We'll see why deserts are often found in the lee of mountains, why deep powerful thunderstorms can form, and why they don't form as often as they could.

We begin by returning to our flexible, closed air parcel and recalling the 3 lapse rates we've learned about: ELR, DALR, and MALR. We've learned that we can't lift hot, dry air very far, but a saturated parcel of air will rise quickly. The state of the rising saturated parcel is called conditional instability, that is, conditioned on the presence of moisture and the situation of saturation. Rising saturated air parcels can be warmer than their environment, but we don't encounter warm saturated parcels at the surface very often. Instead, air typically starts at subsaturation, cooling faster than the ELR before finally becoming saturated. If we lift a subsaturated air parcel, its temperature decreases at the DALR. The dew point of the parcel also decreases at about 2°C per kilometer. That's the dew point lapse rate. The dew point decreases because the volume of the parcel increases as it ascends; the water vapor in the parcel spreads out.

A film clip of clouds in motion shows this dry adiabatic approach to saturation, followed by a moist adiabatic ascent above cloud base. At cloud base, temperature and dew point of a subsaturated air parcel are both the same and both lower than when they started. We now have a cloud, extending from the LCL up the mountaintop. If the parcel is positively buoyant, it continues to rise and creates a deep convective cloud. If it's negatively buoyant (colder than its surroundings), it will sink back down the leeside of the mountain.

Now let's look at a thunderstorm sounding, a case in which it's possible for a surface parcel to become positively buoyant on ascent despite starting off subsaturated and struggling. A subsaturated parcel lifted to LCL is negatively buoyant, but if a front pushes the air aloft, the now-saturated parcel will follow the moist adiabat and become warmer than its surroundings. It reaches its level of free convection (LFC) and is positively buoyant. Ultimately, the rising parcel will exhaust its supply of water vapor and cool down to the same temperature as its surroundings. This is its equilibrium level (EQL), also called cloud top. The main part of the cloud is warmer than its surroundings and positively buoyant. The lower section, between the LCL and LFC, is colder, as is the top part of the cloud, slightly above the EQL.

Let's consider the region of positive buoyancy. The area from the LFC to the EQL represents potential energy (called convective available potential energy, or CAPE) that can be used by the parcel to rise. Before the CAPE can be tapped, negative buoyancy must be overcome. That's the negative area on our sounding, called convective inhibition (CIN). Our sounding has an LFC for surface air, and that air can become positively buoyant if lifted high enough, but it doesn't always have the means to reach LFC.

Roll clouds result from strong uneven heating of the land. As the land heats up, the relative humidity decreases because, typically, the vapor supply does not change.

Let's return to the sea breeze, which often initiates thunderstorms. On the beach, the land surface heats up during the day, and the thickness of the layer between 2 isobars increases. Air rises over the land and spreads toward the sea, creating a pressure difference between land air and sea air. The cool sea air starts moving inland. When the cooler air from the sea collides with the warmer air over the land, a front is formed. The sea air burrows beneath the less dense air over land, forcing the land air to rise over the sea breeze front. If the land air is sufficiently moist, and if the frontal lifting is strong and deep enough, the land air can be lifted to its LCL. If the land air reaches its LFC, the sea breeze lifting can provoke deep convection, leading to strong winds; heavy rain; and possibly, thunderstorms.

Roll clouds result from strong uneven heating of the land. As the land heats up, the relative humidity decreases because, typically, the vapor supply does not change. That would make it seem harder to create a cloud by lifting. We can bring a parcel of subsaturated surface air to saturation at 600 meters, but this parcel will always be negatively buoyant. As the land surface heats up during the day, however, the ELR increases near the surface. At this point, the temperature and the vapor capacity have increased, but the dew point and the vapor supply have not; thus, the air now has a lower relative humidity. To make a cloud from this surface air, we have to lift it even farther, but there's much less resistance to lifting. Even though it's easier to lift, our air parcel doesn't remain positively buoyant very long and will probably not get much above its LCL. The result is a string of tiny clouds. ■

Questions to Consider

1. How might thunderstorms be different, in intensity and/or depth, if all of the atmosphere's ozone completely and permanently disappeared?

2. You heat a vessel full of water. After it starts boiling, you remove the vessel from the heat and set it aside. After the boiling motion ceases, you dip a metal spoon into the upper layer of the water. The water begins boiling again. Why?

Whence and Whither the Wind, Part 1
Lecture 11

If we applied the sea breeze model to the Northern Hemisphere, we would see it predicting a surface wind blowing from the cold north to the warm south, from the pole towards the equator—but sustained surface winds don't blow north and south in very many places.

In this lecture, we examine forces that work counter to nature's tendency to push air from high to low pressure, from colder places (the north) to warmer places (the south). The 4 principal forces that determine where, when, and how quickly the horizontal wind blows are pressure gradient force (PGF), the Coriolis force, frictional force, and a centripetal or centrifugal force. In this lecture, we'll discuss the first 2 of these forces and learn how they participate in determining how and where the wind blows.

A pressure gradient is a pressure difference divided by a distance. Pressure differences drive winds, but pressure gradients determine wind speed. The Coriolis force owes its existence to the Earth's rotation. This force acts to the right in the Northern Hemisphere and to the left in the Southern Hemisphere; it vanishes at the equator.

During World War I, the Germans deployed a long-range cannon, the Paris Gun, directly east of Paris and fired shells at the city. According to some accounts, the Germans failed to take the Coriolis effect into account, and many of their shells fell to the north of Paris. A rocket fired at the North Pole travels straight, but from our point of view, it seems to curve to the right because what we call north is not fixed in time. Our compass directions also vary in space due to the fact that the Earth is a sphere. A rocket fired to the west cannot travel without a change of latitude because the Earth is curved, and latitude circles are curved, as well. We explain this apparent deflection with another convenient untruth, the curvature force.

In the incident from World War II, the curvature force was working in the opposite direction to Coriolis. Coriolis tried to deflect the shells to the north, while from our point of view, curvature pushed them to the south. In fact, based on the reported shell velocity, the curvature deflection would exceed the Coriolis deflection, and the Paris Gun shells should have missed Paris to the south.

Why does the Coriolis force act to the left, following the motion in the Southern Hemisphere? And why does this force vanish at the equator? Seen from above the North Pole, the Northern Hemisphere turns counterclockwise. Seen from above the South Pole, the Southern Hemisphere turns clockwise. The Coriolis force acts to the left, following the motion in the Southern Hemisphere. To answer the question of why the Coriolis force vanishes at the equator, let's consider vectors. A vector is an arrow that represents a path and can be broken down into its components.

Think of the spin axis of the Earth as a vector whose orientation is determined by the right-hand rule. From the North Pole, the Earth's spin axis is straight up and down; it's in the local vertical. As we move toward the equator, the vertical component of the spin axis becomes smaller. The Earth is still spinning, but less of that spin is working to rotate the coordinate system at that latitude. The Coriolis force represents the spin vector in the local vertical. At the equator, the vertical component of the Earth's spin axis is zero.

The wind that results when both pressure gradient and Coriolis force are active (active against each other) is called the geostrophic wind. This is the wind balance that is created because the Earth turns.

The wind that results when both pressure gradient and Coriolis force are active (active against each other) is called the geostrophic wind. This is the wind balance that is created because the Earth turns. Consider a pressure difference between 2 isobars and an air parcel. The parcel experiences a pressure gradient force directed toward low pressure. Once it begins to move, the Coriolis force appears, directed to the right. The combination of these 2 forces causes the parcel to deviate to the right of its original path.

The Coriolis force continues to turn the parcel to the right until the pressure gradient force and the Coriolis force are locked in opposition. In this situation, the wind is blowing parallel to the isobars with low pressure to the left. This is geostrophic balance. The wind is not moving toward low pressure, the direction the pressure gradient force is trying to push

Tornadoes strike the United States about 1500 times per year.

it. The wind is not turning to the right, following the motion, as the Coriolis force is trying to push it. Instead, it's a straight-line wind. We cannot disturb the geostrophic balance by pushing large-scale wind harder. Ultimately, the pressure gradient force determines the wind speed, but the Coriolis force is proportional to wind speed. At sea level, if the wind is geostrophic, we usually know that it's blowing with low pressure to the left. Its speed will increase as the isobar spacing on a sea level pressure chart becomes smaller.

The geostrophic wind blows parallel to, not across, isobars. But isobars are not always straight, and to make air flow parallel to curving isobars, we need to add another force to the mix. Sometimes, we can make air blow across isobars from high to low pressure, but that requires another force. ∎

Questions to Consider

1. If the Earth did not rotate on its axis, would we still have winds? If so, what would the average wind direction be in Los Angeles?

2. It has been claimed that, in the Northern Hemisphere, the right-hand rails of railroad train tracks wear out faster than the left-hand rails. Why? (Presume that only one direction of motion is permitted on these tracks.)

Whence and Whither the Wind, Part 2
Lecture 12

In this lecture, we will encounter the other 2 important forces, friction and the centripetal or centrifugal force, depending on your point of view. Friction will help the large-scale wind move towards low pressure, at least a little bit, and in those places where friction is active.

We've already seen 2 of the 4 principal forces that determine when, where, and how quickly the horizontal winds blow: pressure gradient force and the Coriolis force. Let's begin with the third force, friction. The Earth's rotation, through its proxy, the Coriolis force, turns large-scale winds so that they blow perpendicular to the pressure gradient, with low pressure to the left in the Northern Hemisphere. Friction, acting near the Earth's surface to reduce wind speeds, disturbs the geostrophic balance so that the large-scale wind will blow toward low pressure. Friction weakens the Coriolis force. On a diagram, we see the wind blowing from low pressure to the left and Coriolis acting to the right of the motion. Friction opposes the motion, causing it to slow. The pressure gradient force is then able to pull the air toward low pressure, at least at a shallow angle. The result is a 3-way balance of forces in which air can move across isobars, toward lower pressure.

Now, let's consider a different 3-force balance. Wind tends to turn counterclockwise around large-scale regions of low pressure in the Northern Hemisphere and clockwise around highs. These lows and highs are called cyclones and anticyclones. Note that the air flow is parallel to isobars of pressure. This means that friction is absent. The winds' change of direction is usually explained as a centripetal or centrifugal force, depending on one's point of view. The combination of pressure gradient force, Coriolis, and centripetal or centrifugal forces is called gradient wind balance. Centrifugal and centripetal forces exist when there is spin. Centrifugal force is directed outward from the center of spin. Centripetal force is directed inward toward the center of spin. Note that only centripetal force is real. Starting at geostrophic balance, the centripetal force acts in the direction of either the pressure gradient force, guiding the air around the low, or the Coriolis force, guiding the air around the high.

Where did the centripetal or centrifugal force come from? Starting again with geostrophic balance, suppose an air parcel's path takes it toward a place where the isobars are curving in a counterclockwise fashion. Inertia acts to push the air on a straight path, but notice that this would carry the air across the isobar toward higher pressure. Notice that the pressure gradient force, which points most directly toward low pressure, opposes inertia. Part of the wind's driving force is directed against the parcel, and the air must slow down.

When the air slows down, the Coriolis force is reduced, allowing the pressure gradient force to change the direction of the air, except this time, it doesn't result in cross-isobar flow. Instead, the parcel continues to follow the isobars as they curve. Thus, we've made a cyclone with air curving counterclockwise around low pressure. If the air parcel approaches isobars that are curving clockwise, inertia will carry it toward lower pressure. A component of the pressure gradient force is now pointing in the direction of parcel motion. The parcel speeds up, increasing the Coriolis force, which makes the air bend to the right. The air remains parallel to the isobars but moves quicker than it did when the motion was purely geostrophic.

Let's combine our 4 fundamental forces. Pressure gradient force and Coriolis make straight-line geostrophic flow, low pressure to the left. Centripetal gives us curvature, counterclockwise around low, clockwise around high—still parallel to isobars. Friction gives us a little cross-isobar flow into low and out of high. Notice that owing to friction, wind can cross isobars away from high and toward low pressure. In this situation, the air is converging into low pressure from below. Bringing air into low pressure at the surface creates upward vertical motion in the cyclone. Rising air can become saturated and possibly unstable, resulting in clouds and storms. Meanwhile, the surface divergence out of the high implies downward motion in the anticyclone, and we usually associate highs with stable and clear conditions.

We've seen 5 combinations of these 4 forces; let's look at a sixth. We saw that isobar curvature affects wind speed so that, for the same isobar curvature, as the air curves counterclockwise, the wind is subgeostrophic. The flow clockwise around highs is supergeostrophic. This is an apparent paradox, because we often see strong winds around lows, and we associate highs with weak winds. In practice, isobar spacing around lows can be much smaller than around highs, and that's what leads to the faster winds.

The reason we don't usually see tight pressure gradients around highs stems from the sixth combination of the forces. Pressure gradient and centrifugal force result in cyclostrophic balance. Coriolis has no role here; this is local-scale rapid spin. Spin creates low pressure, as we see when we create a vortex in a glass of water. ∎

Questions to Consider

1. True or False: Space shuttle astronauts in orbit about the Earth experience weightlessness because the spacecraft is so far from the Earth that its gravitational pull is negligible.

2. It is theoretically possible for large-scale wind to be able to blow clockwise around large-scale lows in the Northern Hemisphere. This is termed an antibaric low. For a given isobar spacing, would you expect winds around an antibaric low to be stronger or weaker than their counterparts around a normal low?

The Global Atmospheric Circulation
Lecture 13

Let's apply the concepts of geostrophic and gradient wind balance with and without friction to the hemispheric circulation, driven by heating contrast, owing to Earth's sphericity. Specifically, it's time to consider why the simple sea breeze model doesn't work for the entire hemisphere, spanning pole to equator.

If the basic sea and land breeze ideas were applied to the entire hemisphere, we would have sinking air at the North Pole above surface high pressure and rising air at the equator above surface low pressure. We call the result the 1-cell model. It would represent 1 cell per hemisphere, which would also be thermally direct. The cold air at the pole is sinking, which helps increase its temperature through compression. The warm equatorial air is rising and slowly cooling due to latent heat release. The Coriolis force breaks the single thermally direct cell into 3 cells.

From north to south, the 3 cells are called Polar, Ferrel, and Hadley. Looking at the Ferrel cell, it's colder at 60 and 30 degrees north, but the cooler air is rising and the warmer air is sinking. Expansion cooling and compression warming increase the horizontal temperature gradient in mid-latitudes, so this cell is thermally indirect. The Ferrel cell is forced to operate as thermally indirect by the Polar and Hadley cells.

The 3-cell model predicts surface lows at 60 north and the equator and surface highs at the pole and 30 north. What, then, would the geostrophic winds be? In the Northern Hemisphere, with the wind at our backs, lower pressure is to the left. Therefore, in mid-latitudes, the geostrophic wind is westerly. Closer to the pole, the winds are easterly.

Recall that the Coriolis force vanishes at the equator; thus, the winds there cannot be in geostrophic balance. With the weaker Coriolis force near the equator, we get southeast trade winds between the equator and 30 south, also with a component directed toward the equator. As a result, there is a convergence of surface air at the equator from both hemispheres. This force is sustained rising motion at the inter-tropical convergence zone (ITCZ), a ring of deep convective storms where Northern and Southern Hemisphere air meets. We have westerly winds in mid-latitudes and easterly near the poles in both hemispheres. The only difference is in the tropics, where air is pushed toward the equator from both sides.

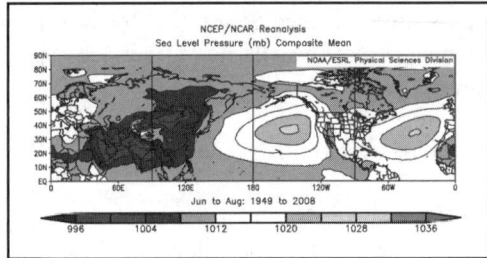

Summer Northern Hemisphere pressure gradient map.

How well does this model hold up in reality? We expect to see low sea level pressure at the equator and at 60 north and south. This shows up well in the Southern Hemisphere. We expect to see high pressure at 30 north and south and at the poles. Indeed, the pressure is higher at 30 degrees, but the picture is also complicated by land/sea arrangements.

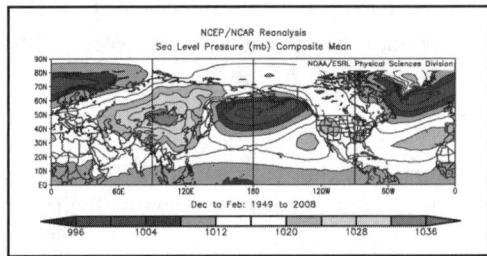

Winter Northern Hemisphere pressure gradient map.

In the Northern Hemisphere winter, the low pressure areas at 60 north over the North Pacific and Atlantic oceans are prominent. The subtropical highs at 30 north are weaker, and the highest pressure is over the Asian interior. In the Northern Hemisphere summer, the Aleutian and Icelandic Lows are absent, and the subtropical Pacific and Bermuda Highs are dominant. In both models, we associate high pressure areas with descending motion, and on a plot, we see that air is sinking in the mid-troposphere, near both subtropical highs. The ascent seems shifted eastward, rather than in the apparent centers of these 2 highs.

At the equator, we see a globe-straddling band of ascent; this is the ITCZ. By adding surface vector winds, we confirm that the ITCZ represents the convergence of the Northern Hemisphere's northeast trades and the Southern Hemisphere's southeast trades. In the United States, the Rocky Mountains create a barrier to surface mid-latitude westerlies. We also see mid-tropospheric air descending, subsiding over Tornado Alley.

Let's compare Northern Hemisphere summer and winter precipitation. We see winter storm tracks associated with the Aleutian and Icelandic Lows in the northern Pacific and Atlantic oceans. In the summer, rising motion over heated land helps create rain in central South America. There is still an ITCZ in the equatorial north Pacific, but a southern branch is also now more apparent. Earth's sphericity has made a temperature difference that Earth's rotation preserves by preventing the ready flow of warm and cold air between places with different temperatures.

An air mass is a large body of air that forms over a particular region, acquiring particular characteristics: temperature, humidity, and so on. Where air masses meet, we have fronts and convergence; not all convergence zones, however, are fronts.

An air mass is a large body of air that forms over a particular region, acquiring particular characteristics: temperature, humidity, and so on. Where air masses meet, we have fronts and convergence; not all convergence zones, however, are fronts. There are 2 primary types of air masses, continental and maritime, and 2 primary source regions, polar and tropical. The 4 air mass categories are combinations of these: continental polar (cP), continental tropical (cT), maritime polar (mP), and maritime tropical (mT). ∎

1. Suppose the Moon had never formed. What would the Earth's weather, climate, and atmospheric circulation be like today? Hint: If the Moon never existed, Earth would likely have a rotation rate *3 times faster* than it does now!

2. San Francisco is famous for its summertime fogs. How and why do they form? Why are they common during summer rather than winter?

Fronts and Extratropical Cyclones
Lecture 14

In this lecture, we'll examine surface weather maps, and focus on the lifecycle of the extratropical cyclone. There are actually 2 basic types of large-scale cyclones, extratropical and tropical, named for where they originate. ... Both are associated with storms. The differences, however, are major.

Extratropical cyclones are strongly connected to fronts. Looking at a surface weather map for the continental United States, we see contours that represent isobars of sea level pressure (SLP). Out West, there is a large area of high pressure. There is also a low pressure system, or cyclone, in the Ohio Valley. The winds are generally curving clockwise around an amorphous region of high pressure across the Rockies. Other things being equal, clockwise-curving air flow will be faster than counterclockwise-curving flow, but that doesn't often happen around highs.

Let's now zoom in on the cyclone in the Ohio Valley. Note that the winds swirl counterclockwise around the cyclone, but most winds are angled across the isobars toward the low. This creates surface convergence, leading to ascent, one of the reasons we associate cyclones with clouds and storms. The skies are overcast, and near the cyclone center, the SLP is about 1002 millibars (relatively low). The 4 basic types of fronts are cold,

Note that the winds swirl counterclockwise around the cyclone, but most winds are angled across the isobars toward the low. This creates surface convergence, leading to ascent, one of the reasons we associate cyclones with clouds and storms.

warm, occluded, and stationary. Cold and warm fronts are named according to which air mass is doing the pushing. Looking at a vertical cross-section across a cold front, we see that the cold front is actually the surface position of a dome of dense air pushing against the warmer, less dense air ahead of it.

The colder air is under-running the warmer air, forcing the less dense air to rise and causing clouds and precipitation.

On the Norwegian cyclone model for extratropical cyclones, we start with a stationary front, separating cold and warm air. The winds are parallel to the front, which is why there is no frontal motion. The pressure is low all along the front, but a kink can sometimes develop along the front and launch a more localized circulation. Spin makes or enhances low pressure, so the lowest pressure along the front is in the center of the spin, producing a cyclone. The developing cyclone's counterclockwise circulation starts pushing the air masses more firmly against each other. The dense cold air can push the less dense warm air much more effectively. The cold front starts to swing around the south side of the cyclone.

As the fast-moving cold front sweeps around the cyclone, it catches up with the slow-moving warm front, first near the cyclone center. This forms the occluded front. As the occlusion advances, the cold and warm fronts zip up like a zipper, starting at the low, then proceeding on away. Precipitation associated with the cyclone may be heaviest now. The occluded low decays rapidly because the horizontal density contrast that the cyclone started with diminishes.

Let's return to our original cyclone to compare its life cycle with the textbook example. Our cyclone formed along a stationary front, which extended along the Gulf Coast and developed into snowstorms in the eastern United States. The cyclone evolves rapidly as it moves northeastward. As it moves over Ohio, it is fully occluded, cut off from the front. Two new cyclones are developing in South Carolina and Delaware; of the 2 new storms, the northeast cyclone survives long enough to occlude. We also see bands of precipitation in the warm air area, ahead of the cold front. These are prefrontal squall lines, where the heaviest rain and most severe weather could occur.

We described our surface map as a map of sea level pressure, but virtually all areas shown are above sea level, so the elevation of sea level would be underground. How do we get a pressure for sea level when the sea level is underground? Picture 2 stations, 1 located at sea level and 1 located on an inland plateau, 1 kilometer above sea level. Will the wind between these stations be directed offshore or onshore? The station pressures at the 2 locations may be 1000 and 900 millibars, respectively, but that largely reflects the 1-kilometer difference in elevation. To determine the sign and magnitude of the pressure gradient force between these 2 stations, we need to adjust all the surface pressures to a common elevation—sea level. ■

Suggested Reading

Kocin and Uccellini, "Northeast Snowstorms."

Questions to Consider

1. Sketch a station model for a location with easterly winds at 55 knots; an obscured sky; a temperature and dew point of 50°F and 45°F, respectively; and a sea-level pressure of 1006.6 mb. By the way, take a guess at the station's wet bulb temperature.

2. Freezing rain is precipitation that reaches the surface as super cooled liquid and then freezes on contact with any object it encounters. This type of precipitation is more common with warm fronts than cold fronts. Why?

Middle Troposphere—Troughs and Ridges
Lecture 15

So let's consider again the north/south temperature difference between the pole and the equator, and let's keep in mind that pressure changes with height much more quickly than in the horizontal.

Instead of plotting pressure variations on a constant height chart, let's focus on height variations on a constant pressure chart. If we look at a 500-millibar isobaric chart, averaged between December and February, the pressure everywhere is 500 millibars. Near the pole, the 500-millibar height is 5000 geopotential meters (gpm). In the tropics, it's over 5800 gpm. The gpm is a vertical distance adjusted for variations of Earth's gravity with height. On the chart, note that there are horizontal pressure gradients when isobaric surfaces are sloped. Thus, the pressure gradient force on an isobaric chart is represented by height gradients. Where height contours are more packed, the winds are faster.

In a 500-millibar chart for the cyclone from the last lecture, the lowest heights are in northern Canada, and the winds are generally west to east. The height contours reveal a high-amplitude, large-scale wavy structure. We call these planetary waves. The places in the waves where the height contours dip farther to the south are troughs, and ridges are axes of locally higher heights.

One of the 2 mechanisms for producing deep tropospheric ascent is warm advection. Warm advection takes place when a southerly wind with warm air displaces cold air to the north. At the 1000- to 500-millibar layer in the vertical plane, both the average temperature and the thickness of the layer increase. The thickness increase implies that the air must be rising. The same mass is occupying a greater depth as a function of time.

The second mechanism is vorticity. Vorticity is defined relative to the orientation of the spin axis; thus, vorticity in a horizontal plane is called vertical vorticity, and vorticity in a vertical plane is horizontal vorticity. There are 2 sources for vorticity: the spin of the Earth, which we call planetary vorticity; and the spin relative to the Earth, which we call relative vorticity. We saw planetary vorticity earlier when we discussed the Coriolis force. The Earth's Northern Hemisphere, as seen from above, spins counterclockwise. This is positive planetary vorticity (f). Relative vertical vorticity is spin relative to the Earth. We refer to this with the Greek lowercase letter ζ. An extratropical cyclone has positive relative vorticity, due to its counterclockwise spin, and positive planetary vorticity, due to the Earth's spin. The cyclone's total, or absolute, vorticity is $f + \zeta$.

At the equator, f is zero, but in the mid-latitudes, absolute vorticity is usually positive, even with clockwise circulation, as around highs. With an extratropical cyclone and a cyclone, the flow is counterclockwise around the low and clockwise around the high. Around the low pressure, we have positive relative vorticity; because the Earth is rotating counterclockwise, we have positive planetary vorticity, as well. The anticyclone's relative vorticity is negative (clockwise flow), but because f is positive and large, absolute vorticity is positive.

Relative vorticity has 2 main components, curvature vorticity and shear vorticity. We see curvature vorticity in the circular flow around lows and highs. We can also have vorticity when the flow is straight, as long as it is shear. Shear refers to a change of wind speed, direction, or both over a distance. Curvature vorticity and shear vorticity are 2 contributions to relative vorticity. In some situations, they cancel each other out. We often find local maxima of absolute vorticity in troughs, where curvature and shear vorticity can constructively reinforce each other. We call this a vorticity maximum, or a vort max.

PVA doesn't just create low pressure at the surface; it also increases spin and helps move troughs eastward.

Absolute vorticity is a property of the flow that can be advected by the winds. Positive vorticity advection (PVA) will occur downwind of a vorticity maximum. PVA can induce upward motion, creating upper-level divergence that can decrease or maintain the surface low pressure of a cyclone. In a vertical cross-section of a cyclone, PVA is taking place at 500 millibars. Recall that vorticity is spin, and spin creates lower pressure. That's the cyclostrophic effect. The pressure drops where the PVA is occurring, which pushes the 500-millibar level to a lower altitude. This increases the vertical pressure gradient and decreases the thickness of the 1000- to 500-millibar layer due to expansion cooling.

The ascent of mass in this column forces outflow, causing the surface pressure to drop. In this process, we can create a cyclone that didn't already exist or strengthen an existing cyclone. Note that PVA must increase with height and that the PVA-produced ascent involves cooling. If the 2 processes (decreasing the thickness of the layer with cooling and increasing it through warming) took place at the same time, they would cancel out.

Why do troughs move eastward? Why do extratropical cyclones decay? PVA doesn't just create low pressure at the surface; it also increases spin and helps move troughs eastward. If the trough catches up with the surface low, the system becomes vertically stacked. The PVA is no longer above the surface low, which means that the cyclone will decay. ■

Suggested Reading

Kocin and Uccellini, "Northeast Snowstorms."

Martin, *Mid-Latitude Atmospheric Dynamics*.

Questions to Consider

1. A "cut-off" low at the 500 mb level consists of a closed, cyclonic circulation embedded in a planetary wave trough. The air in the low can be quite cold. When such a low moves over southern California during the warm season, thunderstorms can occur. Why?

2. Explain how PVA and warm advection can cancel each other out if they take place at the same location and time.

Wind Shear—Horizontal and Vertical
Lecture 16

In the last lecture, we saw there were 2 somewhat contradictory and competitive ways of producing deep tropospheric ascent, leading to upper-level divergence, that could ... intensify the surface low: warm advection and positive vorticity advection, which we call "PVA." They used very different means to get the job done.

In this lecture, we'll use many of the concepts we've acquired during the course thus far to further examine shear, both vertical and horizontal. We'll also put some of the final touches on our picture of atmospheric circulation. We'll see that our atmosphere's circulation is a function of latitude, height, and time. In the last lecture, we saw warm advection and PVA as somewhat competitive ways to deepen a surface extratropical cyclone by evacuating air out of a column above the low. Both are characterized by establishing divergence in the middle to upper troposphere. We noted that lower 500-millibar heights were generally located near the pole, where the air is colder and the thicknesses are smaller.

We can also look at the 200-millibar level, which is near the tropopause in mid-latitudes. In the Northern Hemisphere, geostrophic wind blows with lower height to the left. The narrower the contour separation, the faster the winds are. What we're really seeing, though, is diffluence (flowing away). The winds are moving away from each other, but they're also slowing down because the height contour spacing is widening.

One feature to watch for on upper-level charts are jets, which are tubes of high-velocity air. We see a jet tube intersecting an isobaric surface, such as the 200-millibar level. The contours there are isotachs, lines of constant wind speed. Along the jet axis, we see divergence on the rear side of the jet streak and convergence ahead. There's no curvature to these winds, but there is horizontal shear. This shear induces counterclockwise positive relative vorticity on the north side of the jet streak and clockwise negative relative vorticity on the south side.

Let's consider the 4 quadrants of the jet. PVA will induce ascent in the left exit and right entrance quadrants. This pattern of rising and sinking motion will induce a secondary circulation. At the jet streak level, the ascent and descent should create a flow heading south from the exit region. The air is rising on the north side of the exit region and sinking on the south side; thus, there should be a wind at this level that is blowing from north to south. The secondary circulation loop is closed by realizing that that has to occur in the lower troposphere. That low-level flow can play an important role in enhancing moisture advection from the Gulf to the midwestern United States.

At the jet streak level, the ascent and descent should create a flow heading south from the exit region. The air is rising on the north side of the exit region and sinking on the south side; thus, there should be a wind at this level that is blowing from north to south.

Why does wind speed tend to increase with height in the troposphere? In other words, why do we have vertical wind shear? For the most part, the reason the average westerly wind increases in magnitude with height in the mid-latitude troposphere is that it's colder to the north. In addition to creating pressure differences that drive winds, temperature differences cause vertical wind shear. On a diagram, we see the 1000-millibar level with no pressure gradient force. The fact that it's colder in the north means that the vertical distance between the 1000- and 750-millibar layer will vary with latitude. Looking at the 750- to 500-millibar layer, the horizontal pressure gradient force is even greater at 500 millibars, resulting in a stronger wind.

At 250 millibars, we reach the level of maximum wind. The 250- to 100-millibar layer is thicker to the north, which means that the isobaric surface at the top of that layer tilts somewhat less than it did at the bottom of the layer, and the wind gets weaker. In the north, the 250- to 100-millibar layer is in the stratosphere, where temperature stops decreasing with height. In the south, the same layer is still in the troposphere and getting colder with height. The tropopause level varies greatly with latitude. The tropical troposphere is deep, and temperature decreases with height in this layer. Our mid-latitude westerly winds increase with height up to the point where the temperature gradient vanishes.

The location of the jet at the height where the north/south temperature variations disappear is not a coincidence. When it's colder to the north, the vertical shear is westerly, causing a westerly wind to increase with height. We saw this from the surface up to the level of the subtropical jet. If it's colder to the south, the vertical shear is easterly. Thus, a westerly wind should decrease with height, and that's what happened above the subtropical jet. If the surface wind is easterly and it's colder to the north, we would have westerly vertical wind shear. But this means the easterly wind near the ground should decrease with height and change direction to westerly. This applies in the polar regions. Shear gives us a tool to see what wind direction and speed look like above the ground in the 3-cell model.

Finally, let's see how temperature varies with latitude and height. We have 2 isotherms (lines of equal temperature), representing 20°C and 0°C. The more vertical these isotherms are, the larger the horizontal temperature gradient is. Two more isotherms, representing −25°C and −50°C, are at a lower level over the pole than over the equator. It's still colder to the north, but their slope is gradually becoming more horizontal. The −70°C isotherm is over the equator. The tropical tropopause is very cold, and since it's colder to the south, the result is easterly vertical wind shear. In the summertime, we have more uniform heating across the hemisphere. That means weaker horizontal temperature gradients and, therefore, less vertical wind shear. ∎

Suggested Reading

Kocin and Uccellini, "Northeast Snowstorms."

Martin, *Mid-Latitude Atmospheric Dynamics*.

1. The mesospheric jet is located at about 60 kilometers above sea level in the middle latitudes. Roughly, the jet is equally strong during summer and winter, but it's direction is reversed—westerly during the winter and easterly during summer in the Northern Hemisphere. Why?

2. Why does PVA decreasing with height not produce rising motion?

Mountain Influences on the Atmosphere
Lecture 17

In this lecture, we will examine more influences of mountains on the
atmosphere: how the mountains can disturb the atmosphere into which
they intrude from below; and how these disturbances can be felt far and
wide, vertically and horizontally; and how sometimes the mountains
save their most extreme influences for their own backsides.

As we've seen, the Earth's surface has significant terrain features
that can block, channel, lift, and steal moisture from air. Mountain
waves form in a stable atmosphere, so let's review some of the
concepts relating to stability that we've learned in previous lectures. Take
a stable environment, with temperature decreasing at 6.5°C per kilometer in
the troposphere and increasing in the stratosphere. If we make a subsaturated
air parcel and force it to rise or sink, it cools or warms at the DALR, as
long as water substance is not changing phase. Given that the tropospheric
temperature changes less quickly with height than it does for our parcel,
air displaced up or down wants to return to its starting point; we call that
situation stable. This means that the stratosphere is even more stable than
the troposphere.

Let's look at a vertical cross-section of a stable atmosphere. The horizontal
lines are isentropes, lines of constant entropy. The narrower the space
between the isentropes, the more stable the environment. Forcing 2 isentropes
together increases the wind speed between them. Turning the isentropes
vertically decreases the stability of the environment.

How can mountains and mountain waves disturb the environment in a way
that makes the atmosphere less stable? Consider a bell-shaped mountain
standing 500 meters tall. Putting a mountain in the path of westerly winds
creates a disturbance. Air at ground level is forced to rise up and over the
mountain. The resulting mountain waves are stationary relative to the ground,
but they are traveling upward. Where isentropes turn upward, air is rising,
and when they get close to vertical, the environment is much less stable.

One of the most dramatic examples of mountain-associated weather is the downslope windstorm and the hydraulic jump. A hydraulic jump is a sudden change from a thin, high-velocity fluid to a thicker and slower one. We can encourage jump formation by altering environmental stability. We see a profile with a temperature inversion near the surface. In general, temperature inversions can be present in conditions where vertical wind shear and direction—not just speed—are changing with height, resulting in 2 different air masses rising upward from the surface.

A hydraulic jump is a sudden change from a thin, high-velocity fluid to a thicker and slower one.

Temperature inversions can prevent mountain-induced disturbances from influencing the atmosphere higher above, trapping the disturbances in the lower troposphere. We see a mountain that has had a profound influence on air passing up and over the summit. On the leeside, the air plunges suddenly downward, with high wind speeds. This is a downslope windstorm. Parcel paths are also vertical about 50 kilometers farther downwind; at that point, the fast-flowing air abruptly slows down, and that's the hydraulic jump.

We can gain some insight into what ingredients go into downslope windstorms by looking at a simple system, similar to a river flowing over a rock on a riverbed. If we place an obstacle in a free-flowing river, the oncoming flow will slow down as it rises up and over the obstacle, which will make the fluid thicker. Once it passes the obstacle, the flow speed will pick up again and return to its original velocity farther downstream. We call this supercritical flow.

If the initial oncoming flow is somewhat slower, however, the result is subcritical flow. Here, the flow speeds up over the obstacle and the fluid thins, but again, it recovers its initial velocity downstream. To create a downslope windstorm, a hybrid of these 2 situations is required, one that starts out subcritical and becomes supercritical. The flow will increase uphill and downhill. This flow can be characterized by a ratio called the Froude number. The numerator here is the flow speed,

U, and the denominator is $\sqrt{gD}$, where g is 10 m/s/s and D is fluid depth. When the Froude number is greater than 1, we are in a supercritical state.

We've seen a situation in which downslope windstorms could occur, owing to a trapping mechanism. Another way to trap disturbances is with vertical wind shear. The phenomenon called lee waves is created when mountain waves are trapped by decreasing stability or the presence of vertical wind shear. Instead of being able to propagate above the mountain, the waves extend down the lee of the mountain. If the relative humidity is sufficiently high when the air is rising, the vertical motions can lead to clouds, which then disappear when the air starts sinking again. These are the lenticular clouds we saw earlier.

Mountains make troughs, but they also make extratropical cyclones. Consider westerly flow passing over a formidable topographic barrier. If the process involved is dry adiabatic, the mass between the 2 isentropes is fixed. Picture a cylinder of air between the 2 curves approaching the mountain. The cylinder has spin. Subsidence on the leeside can cause the cylinder to be stretched vertically, increasing its spin and creating low pressure in the lee of the mountain. These effects result in leeside cyclogenesis, the formation of new cyclones. ■

Suggested Reading

Durran, "Mountain Waves and Downslope Winds."

Questions to Consider

1. Consider supercritical flow approaching an obstacle. What happens to its Froude number as the air ascends to the obstacle's crest? Can you provoke a down slope windstorm in this fashion?

2. The forecast calls for mid-level warm advection above a mountain range. What is the consequence of this for the vertical propagation of mountain waves?

Thunderstorms, Squall Lines, and Radar
Lecture 18

Radar uses radiation at the shorter end of the electromagnetic spectrum. NEXRAD (next-generation radar) is an example of a pulse radar. It has 2 alternating phases of operation: the transmission phase (the pulse), followed by listening. Waves scatter off radar targets, and the returned energy is referred to as backscatter. The time it takes for the energy to return tells us how far away the echo is. Typical weather or precipitation radar uses a 10-centimeter wavelength, which requires large dish-shaped antennae.

Radar "sees" what's called radar reflectivity. A certain amount of signal—returned energy—could indicate a small number of large particles or a large number of small particles, but radar can't tell the difference. Reflectivity is measured in decibels (dBZ). In precipitation mode, radars execute a series of circular scans at 9 different elevation angles.

Radar "sees" what's called radar reflectivity. A certain amount of signal—returned energy—could indicate a small number of large particles or a large number of small particles, but radar can't tell the difference.

A squall line is a continuous or broken line of thunderstorms with adjacent areas of precipitation. Squall lines are long-lived, unsteady, and multicellular, and they have evaporationally produced subcloud cold pools as their principal propagation mechanism. We see a schematic depicting a squall line in maturity. The leading part is the convective region, with the most intense rain and strongest winds. Behind the convective region is the trailing stratiform region, an extended zone of lighter rain.

Before we look at the vertical structure and air flow through a squall line storm, let's consider 2 important points. In our depiction, the winds are westerly and increase in magnitude with height. Westerly vertical wind shear exists because it's colder to the north, and this westerly shear tries to make the air spin in a clockwise fashion. This spin represents horizontal vorticity. If we change the frame of reference, the squall line is moving east faster than the lower tropospheric winds can blow in that direction, but we still have westerly vertical wind shear.

Let's look at a vertical cross-section across a squall line thunderstorm. A squall line cloud is usually over 100 kilometers across in maturity, and it is the depth of the entire troposphere. Below the leading edge is the subcloud cold pool. The leading edge of the cold pool is called the gust front because the winds gust and pick up as it passes by. Often, these storms are oriented north/south, and they propagate eastward in the mid-latitude westerly winds. However, the storms also tend to move faster than the westerlies, so that the storm's relative flow is largest at low levels, where all the moisture is.

We have a low-level inflow that is colliding with the cold pool's gust front and being lifted to saturation and positive buoyancy, thereby creating the storm's front-to-rear flow. Beneath the front-to-rear flow is the rear inflow current. The rear inflow descends toward the surface as it moves forward because of precipitation that evaporates before it hits the ground. The evaporation of precipitation in this air makes the rear inflow air cold and negatively buoyant. Sometimes this descending rear inflow can bring extremely strong winds to the surface. The freezing level is just about the narrow bright band in the stratiform region.

The thunderstorm life cycle consists of 3 stages: the cumulus stage, the mature stage, and the dissipating stage. In the cumulus stage, air has been lifted to its LCL, then to its LFC, and CAPE is being converted into kinetic energy, driving the air upward ever more strongly. Condensation at this time is mainly in the small cloud droplets, which are being lofted by the winds. The rising air creates divergence above the rapidly growing cloud, pushing mass out of the column and causing the surface pressure to drop. That induces flow into the cloud from below, feeding more moisture into the cloud, but the droplets aren't falling yet.

When the drops get large enough to fall, the cloud has reached the mature stage. The mature cell has rising and sinking motions. Some of the downward motion is caused by water loading. In the dissipating stage, the cloud has reached maximum height. Ice has appeared, but there is little upward motion remaining. A squall line represents a collection of such cells, each at different stages of the life cycle.

If we zoom in on the convective region of our squall line, the depiction we see represents a family of cells, spanning the life stages of a single cell storm from right to left. Focusing on the storm's inflow, we noted that the storm was vertically sheared, resulting in horizontal vorticity. By itself, the shear circulation is trying to make the cloud lean to the right with height in the downshear direction. Why isn't the storm leaning downshear? Notice that the circulation around the cold pool also has spin. This negative buoyancy also produces a circulation, which from our point of view is opposite to the shear's induced circulation. Here, the cold pool circulation is the stronger of the 2, so the flow tilts upshear. A third circulation causes such storms to be unsteady and multicellular.

Let's look at squall lines in a derecho. Squall lines that have a strongly bowed appearance on radar are called bow echoes. Behind these echoes, the rear inflow current has descended to the ground, pushing the gust front from behind. This bow echo is a visual manifestation of windstorms called derechos, the key to which is straight-line winds. We see a representative sounding from the warm sector of a squall line, taken prior to its passage. A surface parcel has been lifted to its LCL, then to its LFC. Once it reaches that point, CAPE comes into play, resulting in tremendous positive buoyancy. ∎

Suggested Reading

Browning et al., "Structure of an Evolving Hailstorm."

Byers and Braham Jr., "Thunderstorm Structure and Circulation."

Fovell and Ogura, "Numerical Simulation of a Midlatitude Squall Line in Two Dimensions."

Fovell and Tan, "The Temporal Behavior of Numerically Simulated Multicell-type Storms."

Houze Jr., "Mesoscale Convective Systems."

Rotunno, Klemp, and Weisman, "A Theory for Strong Long-Lived Squall Lines."

Questions to Consider

1. Radars operate by issuing pulses of microwave radiation, typically at 10 centimeter wavelengths for "precipitation radars" like NEXRAD designed to detect large particles, among other targets. A website claims that if you understand how microwave ovens work, you understand radar. It says that the microwave energy is absorbed and re-emitted by the targets, and the radar then detects the re-emitted microwave energy. Is this true?

2. A strong, negatively buoyant, and moist downdraft emerges from beneath the base of a severe thunderstorm. What kind of environmental temperature lapse rate beneath the cloud is most conducive to preserving the strength of this downdraft as it approaches the ground?

Supercells, Tornadoes, and Dry Lines
Lecture 19

In this lecture, we will see new uses for radar and another type of MCS, the supercell thunderstorm. Let's start, however, by continuing to explore how MCSs get started.

Squall lines and other kinds of storms, such as supercells, can form on or near cold fronts and along other barriers, such as the front range of the Rocky Mountains or a pseudo–cold front called the dryline. The dryline is a boundary characterized by a substantial difference in moisture content. Generally, the dryline is the meeting place between hot, moist mT air and hot, dry cT air. A map of a dryline shows a dew point drop from 68°F on one side to 29°F on the other. Typically, there's a larger temperature contrast across drylines at night. Earlier, this dryline was farther to the west and caused a line of storms to be initiated, some of which were supercell storms. Supercells are a form of organized convection. They're rotating storms and form in environments with substantial vertical shear.

The key ingredient for supercells is large amounts of vertical wind shear, along with CAPE. Shear makes the difference between the ordinary multicellular thunderstorm and the rotating supercell, because spin creates low pressure. In this case, the spin is in a vertical plane, which is useless to the supercell unless it's tilted. Consider a vortex tube inserted in a flow of westerly wind shear. Part of the tube might be pushed up by a thunderstorm, tilting its rotation to a horizontal plane. This creates 2 counter-rotating vortices.

The vortices that are lifted create low pressure on the north and south flanks of the original updraft, but this is not yet a supercell. New storms seem to split off from the flanks of the original updraft; these are the rotating supercell storms. A sounding taken to the east of a group of supercells reveals CAPE at 6200 joules and almost no convective inhibition.

Once the cells split, they tend to move away from each other. Ordinary convective cells tend to move with the mean wind, but split supercells tend to move either to the left (left movers) or to the right (right movers) of the mean winds. The right mover has counterclockwise rotation. In the center, the spin creates low pressure, which keeps the air rising. The updraft is still lifting vortex tubes, so counter-rotations are still being induced on its flanks, just as in the ordinary cell. But now, the updraft is part of a rotating supercell, and the storm tends to move toward the flank that is producing the same sense of rotation. Shear also creates pressure perturbations: low pressure on the downshear side, which is to the right in this case, and high pressure on the upshear side. This also makes the storm tend to move to the east, because the pressure is dropping in that direction.

Many times, the left mover fails to form or dies quickly. A hodograph is a plot showing how winds change as a function of height. Clockwise directional shear enhances the right mover and suppresses the left mover. The shear vector was originally westerly and didn't favor either of the split storms. But with the addition of directional shear, low pressure was created on the downshear side in a position to help the updraft of the right mover.

Sometimes, the right mover radar echo takes on a distinctive hook shape. This is evidence of strong horizontal rotation, such as might be concentrated into a tornado. Frontal boundaries surrounding a basic hook echo shape represent places where evaporatively cool air is colliding with the warm, moist environmental air that's feeding the supercell.

Ryan McGinnis/Getty Images.

The wall cloud is a distinctive feature of the supercell and a possible precursor of a tornado.

Nearby is the main storm updraft, which is being fed by unstable air from the mesocyclone's warm sector. The downdraft air is spreading and pushing the cold and warm fronts around.

NEXRAD can also see winds, in addition to radar echoes, as long as they're directed at or away from the radar's line of sight. This ability uses the Doppler effect, which we know from the changing pitch of a car horn as it approaches or recedes from us. A radar image of a tornado shows strong winds directed both away from and toward the radar. Filling in the gap that the radar doesn't see, we deduce strong counterclockwise rotation.

A map of tornado reports over a 7-year period shows a southwest-to-northeast motion for many of the tracks. The parent storms of the tornadoes are commonly right-moving supercells, moving to the right of north or northeast-bound mT flow coming up from the gulf. Tornadoes are classified using the Fujita scale, which consists of 6 categories based on wind speeds: F0 through F5.

Tornadoes can last from seconds to roughly an hour. Their color comes from condensation and the debris picked up by the vortex. The fastest winds ever recorded were over 300 miles per hour.

We'll close with a few tornado facts. Tornadoes can last from seconds to roughly an hour. Their color comes from condensation and the debris picked up by the vortex. The fastest winds ever recorded were over 300 miles per hour. That vortex probably had a pressure drop of 100 millibars. ∎

Suggested Reading

Lemon and Doswell III, "Severe Thunderstorm Evolution and Mesocyclone Structure as Related to Tornadogenesis."

Rotunno and Klemp, "The Influence of the Shear-Induced Pressure Gradient on Thunderstorm Motion."

Weisman and Klemp, "The Dependence of Numerically Simulated Convective Storms on Vertical Wind Shear and Buoyancy."

Lecture 19: Supercells, Tornadoes, and Dry Lines

1. Consider a dry line, in which the air on the drier side is slightly hotter. Does the moisture difference across the line serve to increase or decrease the density difference? Hint: Adding moisture to air increases the gas constant.

2. The vast majority of tornadoes—sometimes also called cyclones—in the American Midwest are observed to rotate counterclockwise. This is for the same reason that large-scale cyclones do. True or false?

Ocean Influences on Weather and Climate
Lecture 20

In the atmosphere, pressure decreases with height, and the vertical variation of temperature is complex. In the ocean, pressure increases with depth very, very quickly, owing to liquid water's great density. In fact, you'll experience 1000 millibars of pressure just due to the liquid water mass by going down only 33 feet, or 10 meters, into the ocean.

Oceans are important to both weather and climate. They represent a huge volume of water and thus serve as the atmosphere's principal reservoir. Further, oceans serve as a vast reservoir of heat energy. The surface and deep oceans are connected through circulation, in which the atmosphere is also a major player.

Let's look at the vertical variation of temperature in the ocean. We start with a roughly constant temperature layer immediately below the surface. Then, there's a zone of rapid temperature decrease called the thermocline. Farther beneath that is the deep ocean, with relatively small temperature variation. Mixed layer and thermocline depths vary markedly with latitude, longitude, and season, as well as on interannual timescales. Latitude is a fairly good proxy for sea surface temperature (SST), but it is also influenced by the ocean's circulation.

Just as winds do, ocean currents accomplish heat transport. A rough map of the principal surface ocean currents of the North Pacific shows the North Equatorial Current, which carries warm water across the tropical Pacific. This circulation then turns north-northeast along Asia's east coast and, further along, south, becoming the cold California Current. Closer to the equator, the flow is west to east. This is called a countercurrent.

One of the main jobs of oceans is to moderate temperatures. Looking at a map of average surface air temperature in winter, we note that colder temperatures extend farther south over land than over the ocean. In summer, we see a larger difference between the west and east coasts in land temperatures. The ocean's coolest and warmest months are also delayed relative to corresponding continental locations.

The picture of winds pushing surface currents is more complicated than we might expect. The northeast trade winds of the tropical North Pacific push the ocean's surface current southwestward, but the current moves to the right of the wind. The primary forcing for the wind is PGF, but the surface wind deviates to the right of that forcing because of the Coriolis effect. The surface layer current drags the water underneath, representing the primary forcing for the next layer down. The Coriolis force also tries to make that water turn to the right of this forcing. By about 100 meters down, the water is flowing in the opposite direction to the surface wind. This motion is called the Ekman transport.

One of the main jobs of oceans is to moderate temperatures.

If the surface wind is blowing toward the south, the mass in the upper part of the ocean is moving to the west. The *average* transport is perpendicular to the surface wind. Ocean/land differences are also central to monsoon circulation, the seasonal reversal of winds.

An important circulation in the tropics is the east/west Walker circulation. The tropical Pacific has persistent trade winds, angling toward the equator. The Ekman transport pushes water mass generally westward across the Pacific. The flow of water away from the coastlines in the east Pacific creates upwelling, decreasing sea surface temperatures and bringing the thermocline closer to the surface. Meanwhile, the water being carried across the Pacific is heated by the Sun, creating a deep layer of warm water in the west. This layer provides a huge reservoir of energy that drives deep convection and strong ascent and causes surface pressure to drop. The ascending air in the west Pacific spreads eastward, sinking over the east Pacific and closing the circulation loop.

The Pacific circulation cell tends to oscillate in strength and shift around in space over a period of about 2 to 5 years. This is called the Southern Oscillation. The Southern Oscillation results in the warming of the waters off Peru and Ecuador, a phase known as El Niño. The period in which sea surface temperatures are colder than usual is called La Niña. In recent years, scientists have realized that the El Niño/La Niña and the Southern Oscillation are intimately related.

The thermohaline circulation involves 2 properties that determine how dense liquid water is: its temperature and its salinity. The Gulf Stream carries warm water poleward. As the originally tropical current gives up heat and water to the atmosphere, what remains behind in the ocean is colder and saltier. Because this water is denser, it sinks to the bottom of the ocean and starts spreading southward. Much of this cold, salty water flows all the way to the South Pole, where it is upwelled and returned to the surface. This is the thermohaline circulation. ■

Questions to Consider

1. Consider winds, forces, and ocean currents in the following question: How would the climates of the west and east coasts of North America be different if the Earth rotated in the opposite direction?

2. Someone claims that icebergs tend to move to the right of the mean atmospheric surface wind. Is that statement correct?

Tropical Cyclones
Lecture 21

In this lecture, we turn to tropical cyclones, the generic term for hurricanes and typhoons. I'll sometimes refer to them as "TCs." Like their name suggests, TCs are born in the tropical areas of the Earth, but no tropical region is favorable to tropical cyclones at all times, and some never see tropical cyclone development at all.

Tropical cyclones have both similarities and differences with their mid-latitude extratropical cousins. Like extratropical cyclones, TCs are circular regions of low pressure with counterclockwise winds in the northern hemisphere. However, TCs don't have fronts and don't form in places with horizontal temperature gradients, which means that the TC environment typically doesn't have much vertical wind shear.

Let's see when, where, and how tropical cyclones form. Hurricane formation requires sea surface temperatures of at least 79°C, which make the tropical atmosphere moist and unstable. In the Northern Hemisphere, hurricanes generally move northwestward at first, away from the equator, then turn eastward. While tracks often originate close to the equator, they don't form on it or cross it because Coriolis vanishes at the equator. However, Coriolis determines the sense of tropical cyclone rotation.

Two more ingredients in the hurricane recipe are weak vertical wind shear and a preexisting source of cyclonic relative vorticity. A cluster of thunderstorms in an initially calm environment will push air upward, fueled by latent heat release. The combination of latent heating and upper-level divergence causes a decrease in pressure beneath the storms; this low pressure, in turn, draws warm, moist air up from below. The large-scale wind creates a cyclonic surface circulation. Looking at the isobars in the vertical plane, we note calm winds in the center and wind speeds decreasing with height.

Looking farther aloft, the isobars are bowing upward instead of downward. This means that the pressure gradient and the wind direction have reversed.

Vertical shear distorts this process, tilting the storm downshear with height and stretching horizontally the heating and upper-level divergence that helped create the surface low to begin with. The most dramatic hurricanes are noted for the incredible clouds that form the eye wall. For landfalling storms, the worst damage is often to the right of the eye.

Hurricane winds represent gradient wind balance with a little bit of friction. After landfall, increased friction increases low-level convergence into the eye. Surface friction promotes ascent from below and brings mass into the cyclone. It also works to raise sea level pressure. Even extratropical cyclones won't survive this frictional infilling without other supporting ascent mechanisms, such as positive vorticity advection and warm advection. Those mechanisms disappear when the extratropical cyclone becomes vertically stacked, with the surface cyclone beneath its own trough. Hurricanes are already vertically stacked, so they cannot handle the degree of frictional infill that takes place once they pass over land. At that point, too, the tropical cyclone has lost contact with its primary source of instability, the warm sea surface.

Hurricanes are already vertically stacked, so they cannot handle the degree of frictional infill that takes place once they pass over land. At that point, too, the tropical cyclone has lost contact with its primary source of instability, the warm sea surface.

How does the eye form? Consider again a deep convective cloud complex in the tropics, its latent heating and ascent encouraging low sea level pressure, which induces surface convergence. Over time, the Coriolis force will guide the winds into gradient wind balance, with counterclockwise flow around this thunderstorm complex. As the spin increases, the eye forms. The eye wall is the donut-shaped cloud around the hole. Under it, the strongest winds will be found, but note that there is downward motion in the center of the eye, which is one of the reasons that it's largely cloud-free. The eye wall is warm, especially in the upper troposphere because of adiabatic compression. This is called a warm core structure. Farther beyond the eye, the rainbands form.

A numerical simulation shows the development of a hurricane-like vortex, starting with individual thunderstorms. The process starts with a large bubble of warm, moist air over an ocean with a surface temperature of 84°C. The bubble is positively buoyant and soon rises, creating storms. Early on, horizontal

Hurricane Katrina one day before landfall.

convergence into the central area of ascent is obvious, but that eases as the Coriolis effect gets started. Soon, we have counterclockwise rotation and a hurricane. Descending motion in the eye causes compression warming, which makes the surface pressure drop further.

Let's look at a vertical cross-section of the center of a mature hurricane. In this depiction, the hurricane is about 12 kilometers deep and 300 kilometers across. The eye is about 50 kilometers in diameter. Farther out are the rainbands. Most of the flow is going around in circles cyclonically in the lower troposphere, but some air is able to enter the storm at low levels. This is called the radial inflow. Note that the eye wall is slanting outward with height. The explanation for the slant involves the fact that hurricane winds decrease with altitude to conserve angular momentum (radius × spin velocity).

Hurricane Katrina after landfall.

Tropical cyclone formation benefits from preexisting vertical vorticity and thunderstorms. One major source of both is the ITCZ, which has numerous thunderstorms and horizontal shear that represents vertical vorticity. ∎

Suggested Reading

Emanuel, *Divine Wind*.

Stewart, *Storm*.

Questions to Consider

1. Why are sea-surface temperatures often cooler in the wake of a tropical cyclone?

2. After landfall, a hurricane does not weaken as quickly as usual. What factors might be present to help the hurricane maintain more of its original intensity?

Light and Lightning
Lecture 22

Light and lighting—let's get started. First, I'll talk about light and how it moves through the atmosphere. At the outset, let's remind ourselves that the colors we see with our eyes are certain wavelengths of electromagnetic radiation, which also includes ultraviolet, infrared, radio waves, and more.

The colors we see are certain wavelengths of electromagnetic radiation, but color is also partly perception. It is what we perceive it to be. Sunlight entering the Earth's atmosphere can be absorbed, scattered, or refracted. Differential scattering is what makes the clear daylight sky blue. Differential refraction gives us the rainbow. The color of the blue sky is the result of Rayleigh scattering, which occurs when the wavelength of electromagnetic radiation encounters an object that is smaller than its own wavelength.

Refraction also plays a role in the color of the sky. Light is refracted (bent) by passing through the atmosphere. Isaac Newton showed that white light is actually a combination of the familiar rainbow colors. Differential refraction is responsible for the dramatic phenomenon of the green flash sometimes seen above the setting Sun.

The colorful atmospheric rainbow involves refraction and reflection, and both occur as sunlight encounters liquid water drops. When white sunlight enters a drop of liquid water, there's a density change and the light bends. Some of the light then reflects off the backside of the drop and exits the front side again, bending the light yet again.

At twilight, a small amount of light illuminates the upper atmosphere. The sky's color becomes deep blue or even a bit violet. But Rayleigh scattering predicts that the twilight sky should be yellow. There is little absorption of visible light radiation between 0.4 and 0.7 microns. The absorption that does take place is the result of stratospheric ozone and tends to filter out the longer wavelength colors—orange and red. At twilight, the optical path length is longer, and the ozone has a greater opportunity to filter out the warmer colors.

Lightning creates thunder by superheating air. When a lightning stroke occurs, air in a narrow channel around the stroke is heated to 54,000°F very suddenly. Enormous pressure gradients are created, pushing air away from the bolt at more than 800 mph and creating a sonic boom.

As we know, lightning is an electrical phenomenon. To have lightning, we need a charge separation. Lightning tries to bridge the gap between positive and negative charges. Even in clear weather, there is a general charge separation called the fair weather electric field. Under typical circumstances, there is an excess of positive ions in the free atmosphere and an excess of negative ions in the ground. This electric field is about 100 volts per meter, and it's a residue of thunderstorm activity.

Lightning creates thunder by superheating air. When a lightning stroke occurs, air in a narrow channel around the stroke is heated to 54,000°F very suddenly.

How does charge separation in a cloud occur? The negatively charged ground can induce positive charges in ice crystals or hailstones in the base of a deep cloud. The small ice crystals are transported upward by the updraft, but the hailstones tend to gravitate toward the cloud base. Collisions between the 2 particles may transfer negative charges from the ice crystals to the hailstones, resulting in a surplus of positive charges at the cloud top and negative charges at the base. The negative charge at the cloud base repels the negative charge in the ground, inducing positive charge in the ground and resulting in charge separation.

A lightning stroke has 4 parts: 2 strokes down and 2 up. In the first part of the stroke sequence, the stepped leader is created, a stream of negative ions looking for a path to the ground. The stepped leader ionizes the air, smoothing the path for the return stroke, a rush of positive charges from the ground to the cloud base. Many lightning sequences involve 2 strikes in rapid succession. This may occur because the air channel established by the stepped leader and the return stroke has been ionized and creates a favorable environment for the transmission of current. The second pair of strokes starts with the dart leader, which is similar to the stepped leader.

Here are a few lightning facts. CG lightning is most frequent on the Gulf Coast near Florida but rare along the West Coast. Types of lightning other than CG also exist, including cloud-to-cloud lightning, so-called heat lightning, and dry lightning. By putting more aerosol particles into the air, human beings may have increased the incidence of lightning. ■

Suggested Reading

Hoeppe, *Why the Sky is Blue*.

Questions to Consider

1. You are stationary, looking at a distant traffic signal. When the green lamp is lit, you can barely see it. The yellow light is brighter, and the red light is unmistakable. Why can you see the red light so much better than the green one? Hint: The red lamp has the same candlepower as the others.

2. There's nothing special about visible light, other than the fact that we can see it. But, we've seen that the Earth and all of its objects also emit radiation, albeit at longer wavelengths in the far infrared. Why didn't we evolve eyes to take advantage of this ubiquitous radiation?

Prediction and Predictability
Lecture 23

In this lecture, I discuss how numerical models work. The discussion will encompass how we make predictions and what the limits to predictability are. And along the way, we'll gain some insight into the difference between weather and climate.

Newton's second law, force equals mass times acceleration, governs winds and flows. The first law of thermodynamics describes how temperature changes in response to heating and volume changes. The ideal gas law relates pressure, temperature, and density. Finally, the Clausius-Clapeyron equation describes the relationship between temperature and saturation vapor pressure, which determines when water substance changes phase.

In constructing a model, we choose a domain, a 3-dimensional volume of the Earth's atmosphere. A common modeling strategy involves partitioning the volume into grid boxes or grid volumes; the points of intersection among the boxes are called grid points. Data for each grid point and grid volume include such information as temperature, pressure, humidity, wind speed, and direction.

It's important to note that forecasting is extrapolation. Say we know values of temperature, pressure, and so on at some time, t. To calculate how quickly these values are changing (tendencies), we extrapolate from t to $t + \Delta t$. Forecasts may start with observations, but subsequent forecasts are based on previous forecasts. Thus, forecast quality depends on how good the initial data are and how accurate our tendencies are. A model to forecast temperature in your backyard as a function of time will consider a number of factors to identify how quickly temperature should change, then extrapolate into the future.

A numerical weather prediction (NWP) model forecast calculates numerous factors that can potentially influence the weather. How models handle these processes and how well depends on the model's resolution, its grid spacing. Features or processes the model cannot resolve are called subgrid. Factors we might try to resolve in a model include clouds, mountains, hurricane eyes, fronts, tornadoes, and so on. In practice, we need at least 6 grid boxes for a feature to be resolved properly. The more grid points we have, the more time we need to run and analyze the model, and the smaller the grid boxes, the smaller the time step the model can take into the future. Many models have to use a 30-kilometer grid in order to run efficiently. Models are improving quickly, but there will always be features and processes that cannot be resolved.

The roll clouds we see in an image of Hurricane Katrina represent the process of boundary layer mixing. Roll clouds form over land, owing to uneven surface heating. Uneven heating, wind, and a little vertical wind shear can create roll-like circulations. As the land heats up, the rolls get deeper. If the heating is strong enough, if the lapse rate becomes steep enough, and if the vapor supply is high enough, clouds will form above those roll updrafts.

In the early years of the 20th century, Cleveland Abbe, Vilhelm Bjerknes, and Lewis Fry Richardson sought to improve the science of meteorology to make accurate weather predictions. By the 1950s, the meteorological observation network was expanding rapidly, as was computing power. In 1962, Ed Lorenz developed 3 equations intended to describe fluid flow in a cylinder heated from below. These equations were like those used in weather forecasting in that they were coupled and they had nonlinear terms.

Lorenz ran his model twice, using slightly different initial conditions. For a time, the solutions Lorenz used were indistinguishable, but after a while, they diverged. For us, they represent 2 completely different forecasts regarding the state of the system as we look farther out to the future. Even a perfect model will produce such widely varying forecasts from initial conditions that are only slightly different. In this case, the differences were bred in the model's nonlinear terms. Lorenz's experiment was the birth of chaos theory. The scientific term for his results is sensitive dependence on initial conditions.

If we can't produce accurate weather forecasts for next week, how can we trust climate forecasts for the next decade? The answer is simple: Weather is not climate. We see 2 forecast solutions made using the Lorenz model, 1 for sunny weather and 1 for cold. If we average the 2 runs during the period where they oscillate seemingly out of phase, the mean conditions are the same. In other words, the climate hasn't changed. And that's what the climate is: the mean of the system. ■

If we can't produce accurate weather forecasts for next week, how can we trust climate forecasts for the next decade? The answer is simple: Weather is not climate.

Suggested Reading

Gleick, *Chaos*.

Lorenz, "Deterministic Nonperiodic Flow."

Lynch, *The Emergence of Numerical Weather Prediction*.

Questions to Consider

1. If we cannot trust weather forecasts for next week, why should we believe climate forecasts for the next decade and beyond?

2. How could Lewis Richardson have avoided making such an incredibly wrong forecast?

The Imperfect Forecast
Lecture 24

Welcome to the imperfect forecast. The subject here is 2005's Hurricane Rita, which we saw in Lecture 21 on tropical cyclones. The story is why sometimes hurricane motion, hurricane track, is difficult to predict.

We started this course with the perfect storm, and we will close with the imperfect forecast. The subject here is Hurricane Rita, which took place in 2005 and missed its predicted landfall by about 100 miles. We'll look at why hurricane motion is difficult to predict, despite the fact that track forecasting has improved in recent decades. We'll also explore cloud microphysics and its influence on model simulations. Finally, we end with the answer to a question posed earlier: What will happen if you accidentally open the emergency exit door on an airplane in mid-flight?

In September 2005, Hurricane Rita neared the Gulf Coast. Rita was a Category 5 hurricane with sea level pressure as low as 895 millibars and estimated maximum wind speeds of 180 mph. The National Hurricane Center's forecast 54 hours from landfall put Rita on a collision course with the Houston metro area. A few hours later, Rita moved more to the north, and ultimately made landfall on the Texas/Louisiana border. The distance between expected and actual landfall locations was 100 miles.

Of course, each process we parameterize presents the potential for error. We can, however, estimate the uncertainty of a forecast by making more than 1 forecast for a day, a location, or an event.

We already know that forecasts will always be imperfect, and we will always have to parameterize certain factors. Of course, each process we parameterize presents the potential for error. We can, however, estimate the uncertainty of a forecast by making more than 1 forecast for a day, a location, or an event. There are also flaws in our physical approximations, called model physics. When will the LFC be achieved? At what temperature will vertical mixing occur? How can we track cloud particles? The answer is to run the model multiple times, with various thresholds and approximations, creating an ensemble forecast.

To understand the variability in the model results, we need to look more closely at why hurricanes move. The Bermuda High dominates the atmospheric circulation of the Atlantic during Northern Hemisphere summer, pushing around incipient hurricanes over the tropical Atlantic waters. The simulated motions of these storms are related to the intensity, size, and position of the Bermuda High in the model and how well the model's equations evolve the high with respect to time. Two models that place the Bermuda High in slightly different positions with slightly different intensities will put different winds across the hurricane vortex, giving it a distinct trajectory. When that trajectory is extrapolated in time, minor differences in parameterization or reflect resolution can quickly intensify.

Tropical cyclones have a self-propagation mechanism owing to the curvature of the Earth. The 2 sources of vertical vorticity are planetary vorticity (f) and relative vorticity (ζ). Recall that f increases with latitude away from the equator and that absolute vorticity, $f + \zeta$, is conserved in the absence of sources and sinks. The relative vorticity changes induce circulations: counterclockwise where the vorticity is increasing and clockwise where it's decreasing. These circulations cause a new wind to develop across the vortex, directed toward the north.

Let's take a closer look at cloud microphysics. Changes in condensation particles in clouds determine how much heating and cooling occurs and how much rain forms and falls. The size of the condensation particles determines how quickly the particles are falling relative to still air. The size and fall speed of particles both directly and indirectly influence the growth rate. Microphysics parameterization has many "knobs" affecting fall speed, particle size, collection efficiency, and so on, all of which add up to different amounts of condensation, falling at different speeds in different parts of the storm and all contributing to forecast uncertainty.

We started this course with this theme: Nature abhors extremes. As we've seen, extreme weather is a manifestation of imbalance, which nature seeks to rectify. Finally, here's the answer to an earlier question: The next time you're on a plane, note that the doors open outward, but you have to pull them inward first, against the pressure gradient. In mid-flight, against the gigantic pressure gradient, you couldn't open the door if you tried. ∎

Suggested Reading

Fovell, Corbosiero, and Kuo, "Cloud Microphysics Impact on Hurricane Track as Revealed in Idealized Experiments."

Questions to Consider

1. One model intensifies a hurricane more than another one. Under what conditions could this result in a different track?

2. A hurricane model predicts an incorrect landfall location. What could have gone wrong? (You can fill an encyclopedia with your answer!)

Glossary

absolute vorticity: *See vorticity.*

adiabatic: A term referring to processes in which an object's temperature changes occur without heat exchange with the surrounding environment. See dry adiabatic and moist adiabatic. Greek: impassible.

advection: Spatial transport of some property by the winds, such as temperature (i.e., warm and cold advection) or vorticity. *See convection.*

air mass: A large body of air that forms over a particular region, acquiring certain characteristics; common air masses include continental polar (cP), continental tropical (cT), maritime polar (mP) and maritime tropical (mT) varieties.

aneroid barometer: A barometer that uses elastic membranes to measure pressure. Greek: without fluid.

anticyclone: A large-scale region of high pressure characterized by clockwise (CW) flow in the Northern Hemisphere. Latin: opposite of cyclone. Coined by Sir Francis Galton.

barometer: An instrument used to measure pressure. Greek: to measure weight.

beta drift: Mechanism of self-propagation of a tropical cyclone owing to Earth's curvature.

blackbodies: Objects that absorb all incident radiation; blackbodies do not have to be colored black, but that helps.

Bulk Richardson number (BRi or BRN): The ratio between CAPE and vertical wind shear, useful in severe weather forecasting.

Buys Ballot's law: "In the Northern Hemisphere, with the wind at your back, lower pressure will be to the left." An empirical description of the geostrophic and gradient winds; named for C. H. D. Buys Ballot, a Dutch meteorologist.

centrifugal force: An apparent force directed outward from the center of spin. Latin: to flee the center.

centripetal force: A spin-related force acting towards the center of spin. Latin: to seek the center.

chlorofluorocarbons (CFCs): A family of greenhouse gases that were also implicated in the enlargement of the ozone hole; CFCs are or were used as propellants in spray cans, coolants in refrigerators and air conditioners, solvents and fire extinguishers.

conduction: Heat transfer by direct molecular contact; involves transferring microscopic KE, measured by T, from the object with more to the object with less.

convection: Generally, heat transport by mass fluid motion. "Free convection" is self-driven, by positive buoyancy; "forced convection" requires an external agent. "Convection" is used as a synonym for atmospheric circulations driven by latent heat exchange. "Convective initiation" refers to the genesis of thunderstorms, which are composed of "convective cells." Latin: to carry, to convey.

convective available potential energy (CAPE): A measure of positive buoyancy potentially available to a rising air parcel between its level of free convection and equilibrium levels; fuel for storms.

convective inhibition (CIN): A measure of negative buoyancy encountered by a rising air parcel below its level of free convection.

Coriolis force: Apparent force owing to Earth rotation, acting to the right following the motion in the Northern Hemisphere; named for French scientist Gaspard-Gustave Coriolis.

crepuscular rays: An optical phenomenon in which light is partially blocked by opaque objects, such as clouds, trees, etc. Latin: relating to twilight.

cyclone: A region of low pressure with winds traveling in a closed, curved path. For large-scale cyclones in the Northern Hemisphere, this implies counterclockwise flow representing gradient wind balance, in contrast to anticyclones. Types include extratropical cyclones and tropical cyclones, including hurricanes and typhoons. The flow around small-scale cyclones, such as mesocyclones, may be counterclockwise or clockwise and represents cyclostrophic balance. Greek: circle, or circular path.

cyclostrophic balance: The combination of PGF and centrifugal forces; Greek: to turn in a circle.

density: Mass over volume; measured in kilograms per cubic meter.

derecho: A type of squall line in which the thunderstorm band becomes bowed in shape (i.e., bow echoes), often associated with intense, damaging straight-line winds. Spanish: straight.

dew point temperature (Td): The temperature at which air saturates by diabatic cooling. Along with the pressure, Td tells us the air's vapor supply.

diabatic: Temperature change caused by heat exchange—the addition or extraction of heat energy. Greek: passible.

diffluence: Horizontal spreading of an airflow at a particular level with distance and time; can be confused with divergence. Latin: to flow apart.

divergence: Horizontal spreading of an airflow at a particular level that is not compensated by an equal amount of slowing, resulting in ascending motion beneath the level and/or descending motion above.

dry (subsaturated) adiabatic: The process in which temperature changes solely due to volume and pressure changes, resulting in expansion cooling or compression warming.

dry adiabatic lapse rate (DALR): The rate in which temperature decreases (lapses) with height due to the dry adiabatic process; fixed at $10°$ C per kilometer or roughly $30°$ F per mile.

dry line: A moisture boundary common in the western part of the American Central Plains during spring and summer seasons, often involved in convective initiation.

Ekman spiral: Refers to the turning of the ocean current direction with depth in the ocean surface layer. Ekman transport refers to the net motion of the ocean current over the depth of the Ekman spiral. Discovered by Swedish oceanographer V. W. Ekman.

El Niño: A weather and ocean pattern during which the eastern tropical Pacific is warmer than normal. Spanish: the boy child. Cooler than normal periods are dubbed La Niñas. Spanish: the girl child.

electromagnetic spectrum: Comprises the range of electromagnetic radiation, differentiated by wavelength λ. From small wavelength to large, regions of the spectrum include gamma and X-rays ($\lambda < 10–9$ m); UV rays ($\lambda \sim 10–7$ m); visible light ($0.4–0.7$ μm); infrared; microwaves and radio waves.

environmental lapse rate (ELR): The rate at which temperature decreases (lapses) with height; varies with space and time, but averages $6.5°$ C per kilometer or $20°$ F per mile in the standard atmosphere's troposphere. When temperature increases with height, the ELR is negative.

equilibrium level (EQL): The level at which the positive buoyancy of a rising air parcel vanishes; also called a cloud top.

front: A boundary between air masses having different densities. Large-scale fronts include cold, warm, stationary, and occluded fronts. Other types include sea breeze and gust fronts.

Froude number: The ratio between horizontal velocity and the shallow water wave speed, useful in diagnosing downslope wind situations $Fr = \dfrac{u}{\sqrt{gD}}$.

Fujita scale: A scale devised by Theodore Fujita to classify the intensity of tornadoes, based on resulting damage consiting of 6 categories: F0 to F5. Recently succeeded by the Enhanced Fujita (EF) scale.

gradient wind balance: The balance among pressure gradient, Coriolis, and centripetal forces, resulting in counterclockwise (clockwise) flow around Northern Hemisphere cyclones (anticyclones).

geopotential height: The height of a pressure level above mean sea level; in gravity-adjusted units that, in practice, is very close to geometric meters. Unit is geopotential meters (gpm).

geostrophic balance: The balance between pressure gradient and Coriolis forces resulting in the wind blowing in a straight line with low pressure to the left in the northern hemoisphere. Greek: because the Earth turns.

greenhouse effect: Refers to the fact that certain constituents of the Earth's atmosphere—the greenhouse gases, including water vapor, carbon dioxide CO_2, methane CH_4, nitrous oxide N_2O, and ozone O_3—selectively absorb and reradiate longwave radiation, resulting in the Earth's surface and atmosphere being warmer than they otherwise would have been.

Hadley cell: The tropical vertical circulation cell characterized by ascent at the equator and descent at 30° latitude, part of the 3-cell model.

heat: The flow of energy between objects.

heat conductivity: A measure of a substance's ability to conduct heat. Metals have high heat conductivity; air is a very poor conductor.

hydraulic jump: A fluid phenomenon characterized by a sharp change in depth and flow speed, often very turbulent.

hydrostatic balance: The stalemate between the vertical pressure and gravity forces resulting in no (accelerated) motion. Greek: balanced fluid.

ideal gas law: $p = \rho r t$; p is pressure, measured in pascals; ρ is density; t is temperature in the Kelvin scale; and r is a proportionality constant unique to each gas or combination of gases.

infrared (IR): A portion of the electromagnetic spectrum between the visible and microwave regions, divided into 2 sections: near IR (0.7–1.5 μm) and far IR (> 1.5 μm). Latin under red.

inter-tropical convergence zone (ITCZ): Meeting place betweenn and southern hemispheric air.

iso-: from Greek, a prefix used to indicate equal, used in isobars (lines of equal pressure), isotherms (temperature), isotachs (speed), and isoheights. Variant form used in isentropes (entropy).

katabatic: Referring to a wind blowing downslope. Greek: to flow downhill.

Keeling curve: A plot of atmospheric CO_2 concentration with time, named after Charles David Keeling, the scientist who started routine measurement of this gas.

knot (kt): A nautical mile per hour. 1 kt = 1.15 mph = 0.51 m/s = 1.85 km/h.

latent heat: Refers to heat absorbed or released by a substance involved in phase transitions. In evaporation, latent heat is the energy used to break molecular bonds, liberating water molecules. That heat is returned to the water substance's surroundings when the bonds reform during condensation. Latin: to be hidden.

level of free convection (LFC): The level at which a rising air parcel is slightly warmer than its surrounding environment, and thus becomes positively buoyant.

lifting condensation level (LCL): The level at which air can be brought to saturation by lifting, the dry adiabatic approach to saturation; cloud base.

longwave radiation: Radiation emitted by typical Earth objects, being wavelengths > 3 μm and thus consisting of far IR, microwaves, and beyond.

mesoscale convective system (MCS): A large, organized thunderstorm complex, with length and time scales much larger than those associated with individual thunderstorm cells. Examples: squall lines and supercell storms.

mesosphere: Atmospheric layer above the stratopause, characterized by temperature again decreasing with height. Top is called the mesopause. Greek "middle sphere."

meteorology: Greek for "the study of things high in the sky"; the title of a book written by Aristotle around 350 B.C.

millibar (mb): The traditional unit of pressure in meteorology, representing one thousandths of a bar, introduced by British meteorologist Sir William Napier Shaw and formally succeeded by the hectopascal (hPa). Standard sea-level pressure is 1013.25 mb or 1013.25 hPa. *See pressure.*

moist (saturated) adiabatic: The process in which an air sample's temperature changes due to expansion or compression modified by water substance phase changes, but still without heat exchange with the surroundings.

moist adiabatic lapse rate (MALR): The rate at which the temperature of a saturated air sample decreases (lapses) with height owing to the moist adiabatic process. The MALR is extremely variable, ranging from 3° C/km for hot air to almost 10° C/km for very cold saturated air. A reasonable representative average is 5° C/km or 15° F/mi.

monsoon: The seasonal reversal of winds, which often result in rainfall variations and often associated with weather patterns in India and Southeast Asia. Arabic: season.

Newton's second law: Force equals mass times acceleration ($F=ma$). In the metric system, force is measured in newtons (N), which is the mass unit (kilogram) multiplied by acceleration (meter per second squared).

Newton's law of inertia: An object, once placed in motion, remains moving in a straight line with constant speed unless other forces are acting.

nucleation: Aggregation of water molecules during phase changes. The former requires condensation nuclei, especially hygroscopic particles such as dust, sand, salt, and soot. For temperatures above −40° C = −40° F, freezing requires an ice nucleus (heterogenous nucleation), which can be scarce. Cloud seeding involves artificially introducing ice nuclei.

1-cell model: A circulation in a vertical plane in which one branch of ascending air and one branch of descending air combine to form a closed circulation cell.

ozone (O_3): A rare trace gas in the atmosphere, composed of 3 oxygen atoms and located mainly in the stratosphere where it absorbs harmful radiation that would otherwise reach the ground. Greek: to smell.

ozone hole: Refers to a region of enhanced seasonal ozone depletion over the South Pole exacerbated chemical reactions involving man-made compounds, notably chlorofluorocarbons (CFCs).

Planck's law: Tells us how much of each kind of radiation an object produces. The graph of radiative energy emitted versus wavelength is called the Planck curve.

planetary waves: Large-scale variations in pressure on constant-height charts, or height on isobaric charts. Axes of lower (higher) height or pressure are termed troughs (ridges). Also called Rossby waves.

positive vorticity advection (PVA): Horizontal transport of positive absolute vorticity by the winds.

pressure gradient force (PGF): Largely determine wind speeds; a p gradient = p difference over distance; in addition to other forces: friction, Coriolis, and centripetal.

pressure: Force per unit area; in the atmosphere, pressure is largely produced by the weight of overlying air pressing downward owing to gravity. Units include the pascal (1 Pa = 1 Newton per square meter) and hectopascal (100 Pa), bar and millibar, pound per square inch, and inch of mercury.

radar: A system that uses electromagnetic waves to detect the range and quantity of objects capable of backscattering the wavelength employed. Weather radars tend to use wavelengths of 10 centimeters for long-range precipitation radar, and ~3 centimeters for cloud radar. Originally, an acronym for RAdio Detection And Ranging.

radiation: A means of heat transfer in which energy travels as waves at the speed of light. *See electromagnetic spectrum.*

Rayleigh scattering: Refers to the theory of how electromagnetic radiation behaves upon encountering particles smaller than the wavelength of said radiation, used to explain the blue sky and reddish setting Sun, and postulated by English physicist Lord Rayleigh.

relative humidity: The ratio between vapor supply and vapor capacity.

refraction: Refers to a change of direction of a wave, such as light, owing to speed change.

Saffir-Simpson intensity scale: A 5-category classification system used for Atlantic and eastern Pacific hurricanes developed by Herbert Saffir and Robert Simpson, based on maximum sustained (1 min) wind speed measured at 10 m (33 ft.) above the ground.

Santa Ana winds: A warm, dry katabatic wind common in southern California in the fall and winter seasons, in which originally cold, dense air warms dry adiabatically through descent, decreasing the relative humidity in the process.

shortwave (solar) radiation: Radiation produced by hot objects such as the sun, being wavelenghs less than 3 μm and thus consisting of ultraviolet and shorter rays, visible light, the near IR, and part of the far IR.

squall lines: Narrow linear or curvilinear bands of thunderstorms typically characterized by heavy precipitation and strong winds and often trailed by an extensive region of lighter "stratiform" precipitation.

Stefan-Boltzmann law: The relationship between temperature T and radiative energy output E. E is proportional to the fourth power of T.

stratosphere: The layer of the atmosphere overlying the troposphere, in which temperature either increases with height or ceases decreasing, owing to absorption of ultraviolet radiation by oxygen and ozone. Top is called the stratopause. Latin "to spread (horizontally)."

supercell: A type of thunderstorm characterized by horizontally rotating updrafts, often associated with tornadoes.

supercooling: The process of lowering the temperature of liquid water below the nominal freezing point. Supercooled liquid can persist when there is a shortage of ice nuclei and is involved in aircraft icing.

temperature (T): A measure of the microscopic kinetic energy of atoms and molecules, which vibrate and translate, even in solids, so long as T greater than absolute zero.

temperature inversion: A situation in which temperature increases with height.

thermal inertia: A measure of a substance's resistance to temperature change. Metals have low thermal inertia; liquid water's inertia is large. Also termed heat capacity.

thermally direct circulation: Circulations driven by horizontal temperature differences in which adiabatic vertical motions contribute to decreasing the temperature contrast, such as the sea breeze in which the ascending warmer air cools via expansion and the sinking cooler air warms by compression. The vertical motions in thermally indirect circulations enhance the temperature contrast.

thermosphere: Upper portion of the Earth's atmosphere, from the mesopause to where atmosphere fades away.

3-cell model: A simple conceptual model of the atmospheric circulation in a vertical plane stretching from equator to pole involving ascent at the equator and 60° latitude, and descent at the pole and 30° latitude. The 3 cells are termed the Hadley, Ferrel, and Polar cells.

troposphere: The lower part of the Earth's atmosphere, in which temperature generally decreases with height. Greek: "turning sphere."

vapor supply (VS) and vapor capacity (VC): Quantify the present and saturation values of water vapor, expressed as mixing ratios; measured in grams of water per kilogram of dry air.

vorticity: The condition of spinning or vortical motion, identified by the orientation of the spin axis. Vertical vorticity is spin in a horizontal plane, positive for counterclockwise motion. Planetary vorticity (f) is the component of the Earth's spin in the local vertical. Relative (vertical) vorticity (ζ) is horizontal spin relative to the Earth. Absolute or total vorticity is $f + \zeta$, which is conserved in the absence of sources and sinks. Latin: whirl.

Walker circulation: An east-west circulation system in the tropics, deduced by Sir Gilbert Walker.

wet bulb temperature (Tw): The temperature at which air can be saturated via evaporation of liquid water.

Wien's law: The wavelength of maximum radiative emission for an object varies inversely with its temperature, identifying the peak of the Planck curve.

wind chill: Accelerated heat loss owing to convection.

wind shear: The variation of the speed and/or direction of the horizontal wind over distance, either horizontally or vertically.

Z (as in 18Z Oct 31): A commonly used abbreviation for Greenwich Mean Time (GMT), also known as Coordinated Universal Time (UTC), which is based on standard time at the Greenwich Observatory in London, UK.

Bibliography

This course was pitched at the freshman/sophomore level, with a few more advanced topics incorporated here and there. A good place to begin further reading is with the books listed in the introductory-level texts section. The popular books section includes a few accessible treatments of specific subjects covered in this course. The advanced texts are used in undergraduate and/or graduate-level courses that have calculus and physics prerequisites. Some of the scientific literature articles are very technical, others less so. Those articles mainly focus on topics covered in the latter third of the course.

Introductory-Level Texts:

There are many high quality introductory meteorology texts suitable for general education meteorology courses. Ahrens's *Meteorology Today* (along with its streamlined cousin, *Essentials of Meteorology*) is probably the best known; I've used them in freshman classes. Lutgens et al., Aguado and Burt, and Ackerman and Knox cover much the same territory. Danielson et al. appears to be out of print, but is distinguished by a much more "weather"-focused presentation. Rauber et al. focus more narrowly on severe weather in all seasons and does it very well. Successive editions of these texts are generally little changed so older versions are both good and cheap!

Ackerman, Steven A., and John A. Knox. *Meteorology: Understanding the Atmosphere*. 2nd edition. Brooks Cole, 2007.

Aguado, Edward, and James E. Burt. *Understanding Weather and Climate*. 5th edition. New York: Prentice Hall, 2009.

Ahrens, C. Donald. *Meteorology Today: An Introduction to Weather, Climate, and the Environment*. 9th edition. Brooks Cole, 2008.

Ahrens, C. Donald. *Essentials of Meteorology*. 5th edition. Brooks Cole, 2008.

Danielson, Eric W., James Levin, and Elliot Abrams: *Meteorology*. 2nd edition. New York: McGraw-Hill Education, 2002.

Lutgens, F. K,, E. J, Tarbuck, and D. Tasa. *The Atmosphere: An Introduction to Meteorology*. 11th edition. New York: Prentice Hall, 2009.

Rauber, Robert M., John E. Walsh, and Donna Jean Charlevoix. *Severe and Hazardous Weather*. 3rd edition. Dubuque, IA : Kendall/Hunt, 2008.

Popular Books on Specific Subjects:

Comins, Neil F. *What If the Moon Didn't Exist? Voyages to Earths That Might Have Been*. New York: Harper Collins, 1994. Although out of print, this book presents a wonderful set of thought experiments, including the title exercise in which he discusses the role of the Moon in shaping Earth's weather and the evolution of life.

Emanuel, Kerry. *Divine Wind: The History and Science of Hurricanes*. New York: Oxford, 2006. What we know (and don't know) about hurricanes and typhoons, presented in a very accessible manner (Lecture Twenty-One).

Gleick, James. *Chaos: Making a New Science*. New York: Penguin, 1988. A very entertaining take on Ed Lorenz and the science of "chaos theory" he helped spawn.

Hoeppe, Götz. *Why the Sky Is Blue: Discovering the Color of Life*. New York: Princeton University Press, 2007. Hoeppe discusses the role of ozone in the color of the twilight sky, among other appreciations of the beautiful color blue.

Lynch, Peter. *The Emergence of Numerical Weather Prediction: Richardson's Dream*. Cambridge: Cambridge University Press, 2006. An accessible account of the early days of numerical weather forecasting.

Stewart, George Rippey. *Storm*. Berkeley, CA: Heyday Books, 2003. The novel, famous in its own right, but also generally credited with inspiring the practice of assigning names to storms.

Turner, Gerard L'E. *Scientific Instruments 1500–1900: An Introduction*. Berkeley: University of California Press, 1998. Turner recounts the story of the Fahrenheit and Celsius thermometers, and discusses many other scientific instruments.

Vonnegut, Kurt. *Cat's Cradle*. New York: Penguin, 1998. Kurt, younger brother of cloud-seeing pioneer Bernard Vonnegut, contemplated what would happen if an ice nucleus active above the freezing point were to escape from the laboratory.

Advanced Texts:

Bohren, Craig F., and Bruce A. Albrecht. *Atmospheric Thermodynamics*. New York: Oxford University Press, 1998. All about thermodynamics, especially involving water substance. The discussion of why we are not crushed by overflying aircraft is on page 73.

Holton, James R. *An Introduction to Dynamic Meteorology*. 4th edition. Burlington, MA: Elsevier, 2004. The most famous dynamic meteorology textbook; not for the timid.

Houze, Robert A., Jr. *Cloud Dynamics*. 1st edition. San Diego, CA: Academic Press, 1993. Rigorous but readable treatment of clouds and related phenomena, including supercell storms and tornadoes (chap. 8), squall lines (chap. 9), hurricanes (chap. 10), and clouds associated with fronts and mountains (chaps. 11–12).

Kocin, Paul J., and Louis W. Uccellini. "Northeast Snowstorms. Volume 1: Overview," *Meteorological Monographs*, vol. 32. no. 4. (2004). All about snowstorms of the Northeastern United States, relevant to Lectures Fourteen to Sixteen.

Martin, Jonathan E. *Mid-Latitude Atmospheric Dynamics: A First Course.* New York: John Wiley and Sons, 2006. This text provides a rigorous but well-explained treatment of the extra-tropical cyclone, including concepts found in Lectures Fifteen and Sixteen.

Stull, Roland B. *Meteorology for Scientists and Engineers.* 2nd edition. San Diego, CA: Brooks/Cole, 1999. Originally designed as a technical companion for Ahrens's *Meteorology Today*, this text provides the physical and mathematical basis for fundamental meteorological phenomena.

Wallace, John Michael, and Peter Victor Hobbs. *Atmospheric Science: An Introductory Survey.* 2nd edition. Academic Press, 2006. A revised version of the classic textbook, and a good place to start for a more advanced treatment of meteorology.

Scientific Literature:

A few selected papers, mainly concentrating on storms, along with some background for the hurricane track experiment discussed in Lecture Twenty-Four. Technical content varies.

Bluestein, H. B., and M. H. Jain. "Formation of Mesoscale Lines of Precipitation: Severe Squall Lines in Oklahoma during the Spring," *Journal of the Atmospheric Sciences* 42:1711–1732, (1985). This classic paper helps distinguish between supercell storms and various kinds of squall-lines.

Browning, K. A., et al. "Structure of an Evolving Hailstorm, Part V: Synthesis and Implications for Hail Growth and Hail Suppression," *Monthly Weather Review*, 104:603–610 (1976). A famous depiction of the structure of the multicellular thunderstorm.

Byers, H. R., and R. R. Braham, Jr. "Thunderstorm Structure and Circulation." *Journal of the Atmospheric Sciences*, v. 5, pp. 71–86, 1948. The most famous article to emerge from the Thunderstorm Project, depicting the life cycle of the thunderstorm cell.

Durran, D. R. "Mountain Waves and Downslope Winds," in *Atmospheric Processes Over Complex Terrain. Meteorological Monographs*, vol. 23, no. 45 (1990). All about mountain waves, including lee waves, hydraulic jumps, lenticular clouds, etc., especially pertinent to Lecture Seventeen.

Fovell, R. G., K. L. Corbosiero, and H. -C. Kuo. "Cloud Microphysics Impact on Hurricane Track as Revealed in Idealized Experiments," *Journal of the Atmospheric Sciences*, 66:176–1778 (2009). Why cloud processes can influence the direction and speed of tropical cyclones, relevant to Lecture Twenty-Four.

Fovell, R. G., and Y. Ogura. "Numerical Simulation of a Midlatitude Squall Line in Two Dimensions," *Journal of the Atmospheric Sciences*, 45:3846–3879 (1988). Squall line thunderstorms as self-organizing and self-perpetuating.

Fovell, R. G., and P.-H. Tan. "The Temporal Behavior of Numerically Simulated Multicell-type Storms. Part II: The Convective Cell Life Cycle and Cell Regeneration," *Monthly Weather Review*, 126: 551–577 (1998). Describes why multicell storms are unsteady.

Houze, R. A., Jr. "Mesoscale Convective Systems," *Reviews of Geophysics*, vol. 42 (2004). A readable survey of our understanding of MCSs as of 2004.

Lemon, L. R., and C. A. Doswell III. "Severe Thunderstorm Evolution and Mesocyclone Structure as Related to Tornadogenesis," *Monthly Weather Review*, 107:1184–1197 (1979). A famous description of the airflow around supercellular thunderstorms.

Leopold, L. B, "The Interaction of Trade Wind and sea Breeze, Hawaii," *Journal of Meteorology*, 6:312–320 (1949). A famous early paper on the sea breeze circulation.

Lorenz, E. A., "Deterministic Nonperiodic Flow," *Journal of the Atmospheric Sciences*, 20:130–141 (1963). This landmark paper that gave birth to chaos theory is not easily readable.

Rotunno, R., and J. B. Klemp, "The Influence of the Shear-Induced Pressure Gradient on Thunderstorm Motion," *Monthly Weather Review*, 110:136–151 (1982) Why supercell storm split and move at an angle to the mean wind.

Rotunno, R., J. B. Klemp, and M. L. Weisman, "A Theory for Strong, Long-Lived Squall Lines," *Journal of the Atmospheric Sciences*, 45:463–485 (1988). Why squall line storm updrafts tilt against the vertical shear vector, as discussed in Lecture Eighteen.

Weisman, M. L., and J. B. Klemp, "The Dependence of Numerically Simulated Convective Storms on Vertical Wind Shear and Buoyancy," *Monthly Weather Review*, 110:504–520 (1982). Environmental conditions favoring rotating supercell or multicellular storms.

Websites:

Archived Data and Tools:

Archived radar data: http://www4.ncdc.noaa.gov/cgi-win/wwcgi.dll?WWNEXRAD~Images2

Archived satellite data: http://www.class.ngdc.noaa.gov/saa/products/welcome

Archived surface data: http://www7.ncdc.noaa.gov/CDO/cdo

Climate maps: http://cdo.ncdc.noaa.gov/cgi-bin/climaps/climaps.pl

Composite map creation tool (I used this frequently in the course): http://www.cdc.noaa.gov/cgi-bin/data/composites/printpage.pl

The NOAA photo library (hundreds of classic photographs): http://www.photolib.noaa.gov/

Past weather maps from the National Oceanic and Atmospheric Administration (NOAA): http://www.hpc.ncep.noaa.gov/dailywxmap/index.html

http://docs.lib.noaa.gov/rescue/dwm/data_rescue_daily_weather_maps.html

Current Weather:

The National Weather Service: http://weather.gov/

The National Weather Service Doppler Radar page: http://radar.weather.gov/

The NWS Storm Prediction Center: http://www.spc.noaa.gov/

Current and Archived Surface Station Reports and Maps:

Oklahoma mesonet: http://www.mesonet.org/

Unisys weather: http://weather.unisys.com/

Good Place to Find Upper Air Charts and Model Forecasts:

Real-time weather from the National Center for Atmospheric Research: http://www.ral.ucar.edu/weather/

Hurricanes, Typhoons, and Tropical Meteorology:

Central Pacific Hurricane Center: http://www.prh.noaa.gov/hnl/cphc/

The Joint Typhoon Warning Center: http://metocph.nmci.navy.mil/jtwc.php

The National Hurricane Center: http://www.nhc.noaa.gov/

The U.S. Navy tropical cyclone page: http://www.nrlmry.navy.mil/tc_pages/tc_home.html

Satellite Pictures, Radar Images, Surface and Upper Air Maps Forecasts:

College of DuPage: http://weather.cod.edu

Plymouth State College Weather Center: http://vortex.plymouth.edu/

University of Illinois WW2010 site: http://ww2010.atmos.uiuc.edu/(Gh)/home.rxml

The University of Wyoming (atmospheric soundings in real time and archived): http://weather.uwyo.edu/upperair/sounding.html

Severe Weather Forecasts and Storm Damage Reports:

NWS Hydrometeorological Prediction Center (HPC): http://www.hpc.ncep.noaa.gov/

Surface Maps and Precipitation Forecasts:

HPC's current weather map: http://www.hpc.ncep.noaa.gov/dailywxmap/

MesoWest at the University of Utah: http://mesowest.utah.edu/index.html

Notes